All facts, no fiction with CGP!

Quick question — do you own CGP's Knowledge Organiser for Foundation GCSE Maths?

You do? Excellent! Now you can use this Knowledge Retriever to check you've really learned everything.

There are two memory tests for each topic, plus mixed quiz questions to make sure that everything has properly sunk in. Enjoy.

CGP — still the best! ☺

Our sole aim here at CGP is to produce the highest quality books — carefully written, immaculately presented and dangerously close to being funny.

Then we work our socks off to get them out to you — at the cheapest possible prices.

Contents

Section 6 — Angles and Geometry

Section 7 — Probability and Statistics

Published by CGP.
From original material by Richard Parsons.

Editors: Sarah George, Duncan Lindsay, Samuel Mann, Sean McParland, Ali Palin, Caley Simpson.

With thanks to Simon Little for the proofreading.
With thanks to Laura Jakubowski for the copyright research.

ISBN: 978 1 78908 864 9

Printed by Elanders Ltd, Newcastle upon Tyne.
Clipart from Corel®

How to Use This Book

Every page in this book matches a page in the Foundation GCSE Maths **Knowledge Organiser**. Before using this book, try to **memorise** everything on a Knowledge Organiser page. Then follow these **seven steps** to see how much knowledge you're able to retrieve...

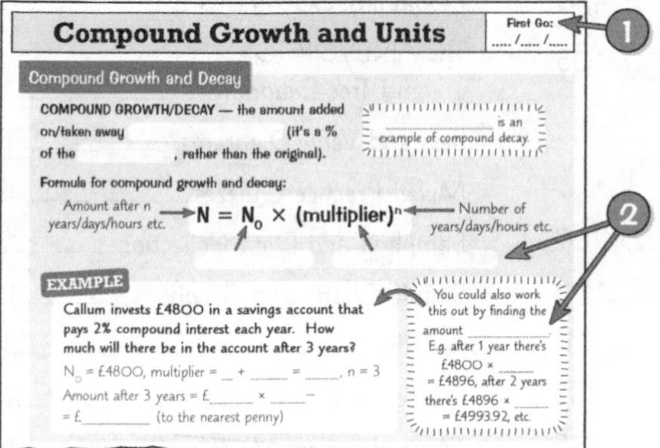

1. In this book, there are two versions of each page. Find the **'First Go'** of the page you've tried to memorise, and write the **date** at the top.

2. Use what you've learned from the Knowledge Organiser to **fill in** any dotted lines or white spaces.

   You may need to draw, complete or add labels to tables, graphs and diagrams too.

3. Use the Knowledge Organiser to **check your work**. Use a **different coloured pen** to write in anything you missed or that wasn't quite right. This lets you see clearly what you **know** and what you **don't know**.

4. After doing the First Go page, **wait a few days**. This is important because **spacing out** your retrieval practice helps you to remember things better.

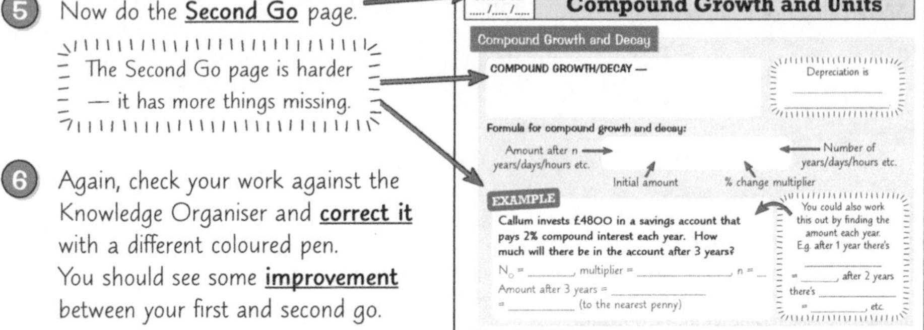

5. Now do the **Second Go** page.

   The Second Go page is harder — it has more things missing.

6. Again, check your work against the Knowledge Organiser and **correct it** with a different coloured pen. You should see some **improvement** between your first and second go.

7. **Wait** another few days, then try to recreate any methods, formulas, tables or diagrams from the Knowledge Organiser page on a **blank piece of paper**. You can also have a go at any **example questions**. If you can do all this, you'll know you've **really learned it**.

There are also **Mixed Practice Quizzes** dotted throughout the book:

- The quizzes come in sets of four. They test a mix of content from the previous few pages.
- Do each quiz on a different day — write the date you do each one at the top of the quiz.
- Tick the questions you get right and record your score in the box at the end.

Numbers and Calculations

First Go: ..... /..... /.....

Four Types of Numbers

	Definition	Examples
	Whole number — can be positive, negative or	–23, –7, 0, 10, 111
SQUARE	Made by multiplying a whole number by	$1^2 = 1 \times 1 = 1$, $2^2 = 2 \times 2 = 4$
	Made by multiplying a whole number by	$1^3 = 1 \times 1 \times 1 = 1$, $2^3 = 2 \times 2 \times 2 = 8$
NEGATIVE		–2.5, –37, –365

Adding and Subtracting with Negative Numbers

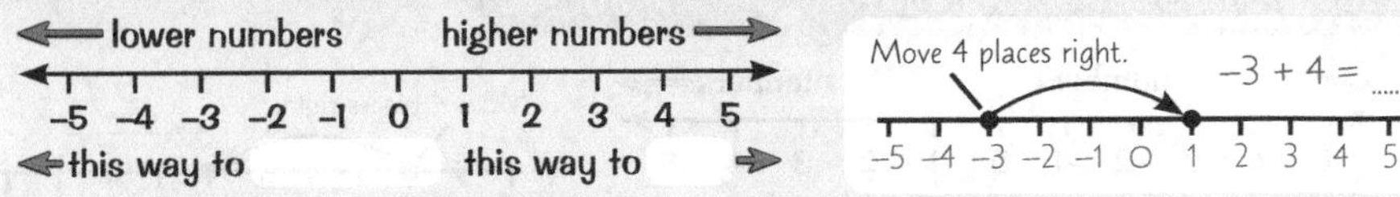

When signs are next to each other:

1. + + makes + $-2 + +5 =$ .... $= 3$
2. + – makes – $5 + -3 =$ .... $= 2$
3. – + makes – $-4 - +1 =$ .... $= -5$
4. – – makes + $-7 - -3 =$ .... $= -4$

Multiplying and Dividing Negative Numbers

1. Signs the SAME — answer → $-3 \times -5 =$ .... $-6 \div -2 =$ ....
2. Signs DIFFERENT — answer → $-2 \times +7 =$ .... $+12 \div -6 =$ ....

BODMAS

BODMAS gives the order of operations:

1.
2. Other
3. Division and
4. and Subtraction

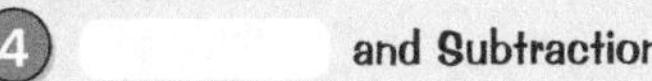

'Other' is things like ....

EXAMPLE

Find the value of $9 - (3 + 1)^2 \times 2 + 5$.

$9 - (3 + 1)^2 \times 2 + 5$

1. $= 9 - \quad ^2 \times 2 + 5$
2. $= 9 - \quad \times 2 + 5$
3. $= 9 - \quad + 5$
4. $=$

$=$

Work left to right when there's only addition and subtraction.

Second Go: ...../...../.....

Numbers and Calculations

Four Types of Numbers

	Definition	Examples
		−23, −7, 0, 10, 111
	Made by	1^2 = = 2^2 = =
	Made by	1^3 = = 2^3 = =
		−2.5, −37, −365

Adding and Subtracting with Negative Numbers

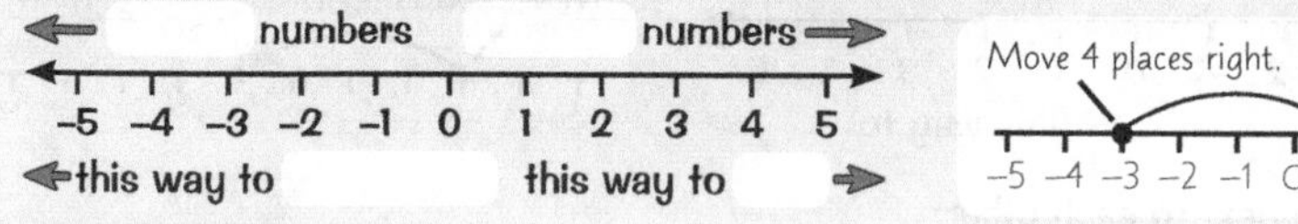

Move 4 places right. .... = ...

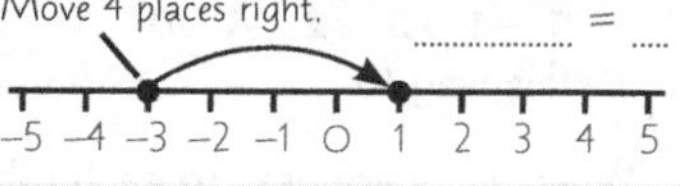

When signs are :

1. + + makes −2 + +5 = ... = ...
2. + − makes 5 + −3 = ... = ...
3. − + makes −4 − +1 = ... = ...
4. − − makes −7 − −3 = ... = ...

Multiplying and Dividing Negative Numbers

1. Signs — answer → −3 × .... = +15 .... ÷ −2 = +3
2. Signs — answer → .... × +7 = −14 +12 ÷ .... = −2

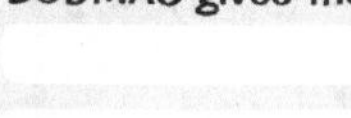

BODMAS

BODMAS gives the

:

1.
2.
3. and
4. and

.... is things like ....

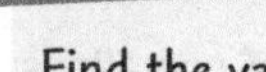

EXAMPLE

Find the value of $9 - (3 + 1)^2 \times 2 + 5$.

$9 - (3 + 1)^2 \times 2 + 5$

1. =
2. =
3. =
4. =

=

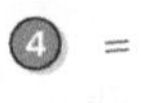

Work left to right when there's only addition and subtraction.

Multiplying and Dividing

First Go: ...../...../.....

Multiplying by 10, 100, etc.

1. Count the number of and move the that many places (↶).

× by 10 1000

d.p. moves 1 2 ....

e.g. 1.52 15.2 152. 152 .

2. Add before d.p. if needed.

1.52 × .... = 15.2
1.52 × 100 = ...
1.52 × .... = 1520 — Fill empty place with zero.

Dividing by 10, 100, etc.

1. Count the number of and move the that many places (↷).

÷ by 10 1000

d.p. moves 1 2 ....

e.g. 120 12.0 1.20 .120

2. Add or remove if needed.

120 ÷ 10 = ... — Remove zeros at the end.
120 ÷ 100 = ...
120 ÷ .... = 0.12 — Add zero at the start.

Multiplying and Dividing by Multiples of 10, 100, etc.

1. Multiply/divide by digit of the number.
2. Count the number of and move the that many places BIGGER or SMALLER.

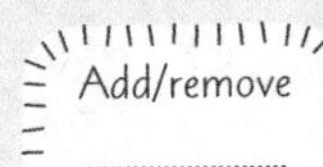

EXAMPLE

Calculate 24 × 400.

1. 24 × 4 = ...
2. .... × 100 = ...

Multiplying Whole Numbers

1. Line up numbers in .
2. Split into multiplications.
3. results from right to left.

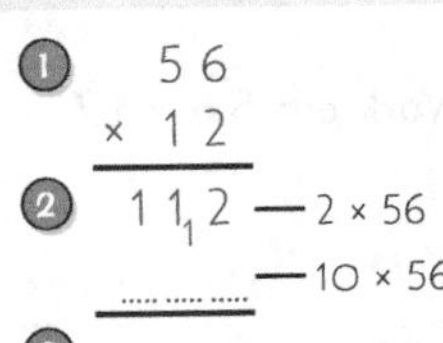

Three Steps to Multiply Decimals

1. Do the multiplication with whole numbers, ignoring .
2. Count the number of digits after the in the original numbers.
3. Make the answer have the number of .

EXAMPLE Work out 5.6 × 1.2.

1. 56 × .... = 672
2. 5.6 and 1.2 have ...... digits after the .... in total.
3. 5.6 × 1.2 = ...

Multiplying and Dividing

Multiplying by 10, 100, etc.

1. Count the
   and move

× by 10 100 1000

d.p. moves ....

e.g. 1.52 15.2 152. 152 .

2. if needed.

1.52 × 10 = ...
1.52 × 100 = ...
1.52 × 1000 = ...

Dividing by 10, 100, etc.

1. Count the
   and move

÷ by 10 100 1000

d.p. moves ....

e.g. 120 12.0 1.20 .120

2. if needed.

120 ÷ 10 = ...
120 ÷ 100 = ...
120 ÷ 1000 = ...

Multiplying and Dividing by Multiples of 10, 100, etc.

1. Multiply/divide by
2. Count the number of

....
....
if needed.

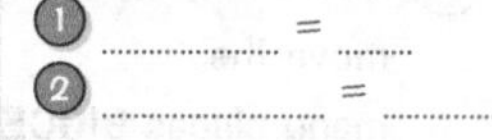

Calculate 24 × 400.

1. .... = ...
2. .... = ...

Multiplying Whole Numbers

1. Line up
2. Split into
3. Add up

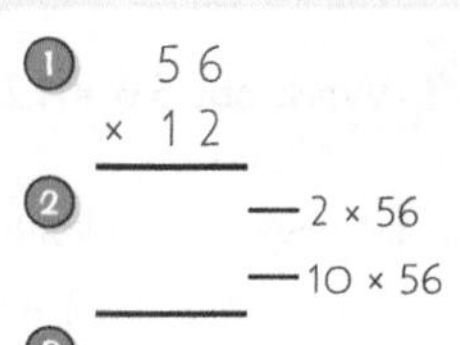

Three Steps to Multiply Decimals

1. Do the
2. Count the in the original numbers.
3. Make the

EXAMPLE

Work out 5.6 × 1.2.

1. .... = ...
2. 5.6 and 1.2 have .... in total.
3. .... = ...

Dividing

First Go: ..... /..... /.....

Dividing Whole Numbers

1. Put the number you're dividing and the number you're dividing by .
2. Divide each digit the line:
   - Write the result the line.
   - Carry the to the next digit if needed.
3. Continue until the is complete — this is the final answer.

EXAMPLE

What is 420 ÷ 15?

① 15 | 4 2 0

② 15 | 4 2 0 — 15 won't go into

15 | 4 2 0 — 42 ÷ 15 = remainder

③ 15 | 4 2 0 — ÷ 15 =

So 420 ÷ 15 =

Dividing a Decimal by a Whole Number

Follow the same steps as above. Put a .... in the answer line (right above the one ....).

EXAMPLE

Work out 62.8 ÷ 4.

4 | 6 2 . 8 — 4 | 6 2 . 8 — 6 ÷ 4 = remainder — 4 | 6 2 . 8 — ÷ 4 = remainder — 4 | 6 2 . 8 — ÷ 4 =

So 62.8 ÷ 4 =

Three Steps to Divide by a Decimal

To divide a whole number or a decimal by a decimal:

1. Write the division as a .
2. Multiply top and bottom by the same to make .
3. Do the division using the method above.

EXAMPLE

Work out 49.2 ÷ 0.24.

① ——

You want to move the decimal point 2 places bigger.

② $= \frac{49.2 \times}{0.24 \times} = \frac{4920}{24}$

③ $24 \overline{)4\ 9\ {}^{1}2\ {}^{12}0}$

So 49.2 ÷ 0.24 =

Second Go:
..... /..... /.....

Dividing

Dividing Whole Numbers

1. Put the number you're

2. Divide each :
   - Write the
   - Carry if needed.

3. Continue until — this is the final answer.

EXAMPLE

What is 420 ÷ 15?

1

2 won't go into

=

remainder

3 =

So 420 ÷ 15 =

Dividing a Decimal by a Whole Number

Follow the same steps as above. Put a .... in the .... (*right* .... *the one* ....).

EXAMPLE

Work out 62.8 ÷ 4.

= remainder = remainder =

So 62.8 ÷ 4 =

Three Steps to Divide by a Decimal

To divide a whole number or a decimal by a decimal:

1. Write the

2. Multiply

3. Do the using the method above.

EXAMPLE

Work out 49.2 ÷ 0.24.

1 You want to move the decimal point 2 places bigger.

2 = =

3

So 49.2 ÷ 0.24 =

Prime Numbers, Multiples and Factors

First Go:
..... /..... /.....

Finding Prime Numbers

PRIME NUMBER — can only be by itself and 1.

- First four primes are , 3, 5 and .
- To check for prime numbers between 8 and 100:

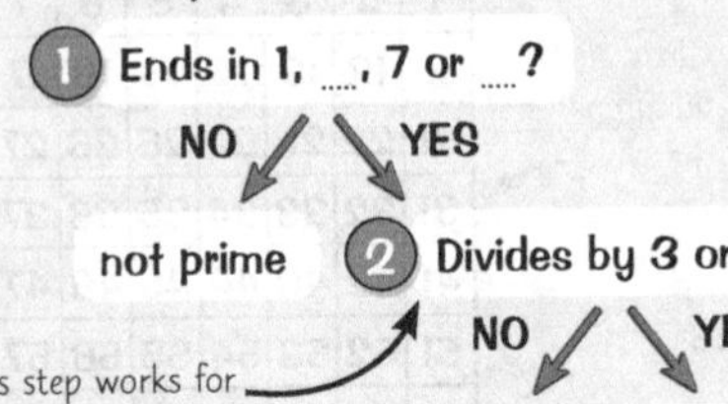

This step works for checking primes between 8 and 120.

1 is .... prime.

1	2	3	4	5	6	7	8	9
11	12	13	14	15	16	17	18	19
21	22	23	24	25	26	27	28	29
31	32	33	34	35	36	37	38	39
41	42	43	44	45	46	47	48	49
51	52	53	54	55	56	57	58	59
61	62	63	64	65	66	67	68	69

Finding Multiples and Factors

MULTIPLE — value in a number's (and beyond).

FACTOR — another number.

Four steps to find factors:

1. List factors , starting with 1 × the number, then 2 ×, etc.
2. Cross out pairs that don't .
3. Stop when a number is .
4. Write factors out clearly.

EXAMPLE

Find the first eight multiples of 8.

8, 16, , 32, 40, 48, ,

EXAMPLE

Find all the factors of 20.

① 1 ×
2 ×
② ~~3 ×~~
4 ×
③ 5 ×
④ So the factors of 20 are:

Finding Prime Factors

PRIME FACTORISATION — writing a number as its multiplied together.

Three steps to use a Factor Tree:

1. Put the number at the top and .
2. each prime.
3. When only are left, write them in order.

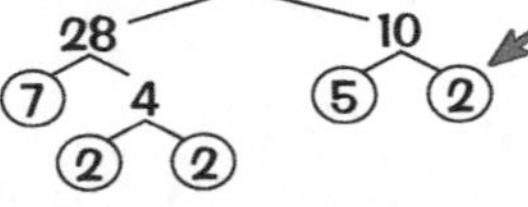

280 = ... × ..... × ..... × 5 × 7
= .... × 5 × 7

Write repeated factors as ....

 ☐  ☐ ☐

Second Go:
..... /..... /.....

Prime Numbers, Multiples and Factors

Finding Prime Numbers

PRIME NUMBER — .

- **First four primes are , , and .**
- **To check for prime numbers between :**

1 is ....

....

1

NO **YES**

2

NO **YES**

This step works for checking primes between 8 and 120.

Circle all of the primes in the table.

1	2	3	4	5	6	7	8	9
11	12	13	14	15	16	17	18	19
21	22	23	24	25	26	27	28	29
31	32	33	34	35	36	37	38	39
41	42	43	44	45	46	47	48	49
51	52	53	54	55	56	57	58	59
61	62	63	64	65	66	67	68	69

Finding Multiples and Factors

MULTIPLE — .

FACTOR — .

Four steps to find factors:

1. **List , starting with , etc.**
2. **Cross out pairs that .**
3. **Stop .**
4. **Write .**

EXAMPLE

Find the first eight multiples of 8.

EXAMPLE

Find all the factors of 20.

1.
2. ~~3 ×~~
3.
4. So the factors of 20 are:

Finding Prime Factors

PRIME FACTORISATION — writing a number as its .

Three steps to use a Factor Tree:

1. **Put**
2. **Circle**
3. **When only**

280

280 =

=

Write

....

....

as ....

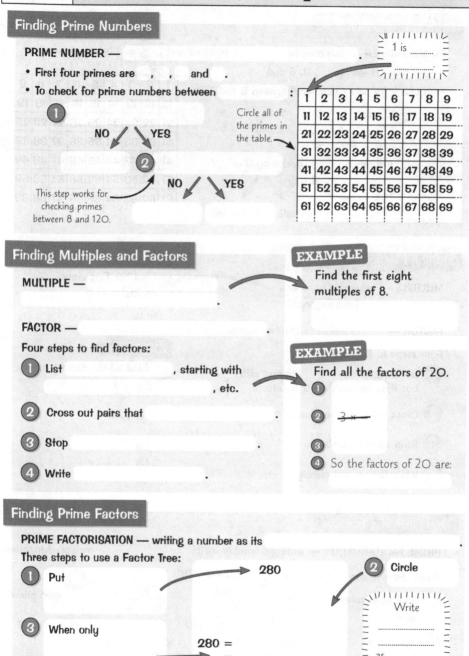

LCM and HCF

First Go: ..... /..... /.....

Lowest Common Multiple (LCM)

LCM — the number that divides all numbers in question.

Find it in two steps:

1. List of each number.
2. Find the that is in list.

EXAMPLE

Find the LCM of 6 and 14.

1. Multiples of 6 are:
   6, 12, 18, 24, , , , ...
   Multiples of 14 are:
   14, 28, , ...
2. in both is ,
   so LCM =

LCM — Alternative Method

Find it from factors in two steps:

1. List all factors that are in either number.
   (If a factor appears more than once in a number, list it that many times.)
2. together.

EXAMPLE

$8 = 2^3$ and $20 = 2^2 \times 5$.
Find the LCM of 8 and 20.

1. $8 = 2 \times 2 \times 2$ $20 = 2 \times 2 \times 5$
   So factors in either number are 2, 2, 2, 5
2. LCM = =

Highest Common Factor (HCF)

HCF — the number that divides all numbers in question.

Find it in two steps:

1. List of each number.
2. Find the that is in list.

EXAMPLE

Find the HCF of 16 and 40.

1. Factors of 16 are:
   1, , 4, ,
   Factors of 40 are:
   1, , 4, 5, , 10, , 40
2. in both is ,
   so HCF =

HCF — Alternative Method

Find it from factors in two steps:

1. List all factors that are in numbers.
2. together.

EXAMPLE

$36 = 2^2 \times 3^2$ and $60 = 2^2 \times 3 \times 5$.
Find the HCF of 36 and 60.

1. $36 = 2 \times 2 \times 3 \times 3$
   $60 = 2 \times 2 \times 3 \times 5$
   So factors in numbers are 2, 2, 3
2. HCF = =

Second Go:
..... /..... /.....

LCM and HCF

Lowest Common Multiple (LCM)

LCM —

in question.

Find it in two steps:

1. List
2. Find the

EXAMPLE

Find the LCM of 6 and 14.

1. Multiples of 6 are:

   Multiples of 14 are:

2. ,

   so LCM =

LCM — Alternative Method

Find it from prime factors in two steps:

1. List

   (If a factor appears more than once in a number, list it that many times.)

2.

EXAMPLE

$8 = 2^3$ and $20 = 2^2 \times 5$.
Find the LCM of 8 and 20.

1. 8 = 20 =

   So in

   are

2. LCM = =

Highest Common Factor (HCF)

HCF —

in question.

Find it in two steps:

1. List
2. Find the

EXAMPLE

Find the HCF of 16 and 40.

1. Factors of 16 are:

   Factors of 40 are:

2. ,

   so HCF =

HCF — Alternative Method

Find it from prime factors in two steps:

1. List
2.

EXAMPLE

$36 = 2^2 \times 3^2$ and $60 = 2^2 \times 3 \times 5$.
Find the HCF of 36 and 60.

1. 36 =

   60 =

   So in

   are

2. HCF = =

Mixed Practice Quizzes

BODMAS, LCM, HCF... pah, where are my QFQs? What? Oh, you mean quick-fire quizzes? They're right here, covering everything on p.3-12.

Quiz 1

Date: ...... / ...... / ......

1) True or false? All prime numbers bigger than 5 end in 1, 3, 7 or 9.
2) What is an integer?
3) When should you stop listing pairs of numbers when finding factors?
4) True or false? $8.62 \times 1000 = 862$.
5) How would you set up $780 \div 12$ to work it out using short division?
6) On a number line, which way do you move to subtract?
7) What is prime factorisation?
8) True or false? The highest common factor of 30 and 45 is 15.
9) When you multiply a number by 10, how many places bigger do you move the decimal point?
10) How do you find the lowest common multiple using prime factors?

Total:

Quiz 2

Date: ...... / ...... / ......

1) If you multiply two negative numbers together, will the answer be positive or negative?
2) What should you circle in a factor tree?
3) When you divide a number by 100, how many places smaller do you move the decimal point?
4) What is a square number?
5) What does the completed top line of a short division calculation show?
6) How do you find the highest common factor using prime factors?
7) What do the letters BODMAS stand for?
8) What is a prime number?
9) Is 30 a multiple of 12?
10) How would you use $38 \times 24 = 912$ to work out 3.8×2.4?

Total:

Mixed Practice Quizzes

Quiz 3

Date: ...... / ...... / ......

1) What is a factor of a number?
2) If you work out $1530 \div 10 = 153.0$, what last step do you need to do?
3) Is the answer to $5 - -8$ positive or negative?
4) In the calculation $4 \times 3 + 2$, what should be carried out first: the addition or the multiplication?
5) After lining up 32×17 in columns, which two multiplications should you split the calculation into?
6) The prime factors that appear in both of two numbers are 2, 3, 3 and 5. What is the highest common factor of the two numbers?
7) What are the first four square numbers?
8) How would you use $65 \times 3 = 195$ to work out 65×300?
9) What would be the first step in working out $36 \div 0.15$?
10) What is a lowest common multiple?

Total:

Quiz 4

Date: ...... / ...... / ......

1) What is a cube number?
2) What is a highest common factor?
3) What is the first thing you should do to work out 23×2000?
4) What is the lowest common multiple of 4 and 5?
5) What are the first four prime numbers?
6) Is the answer to $-6 \div 3$ positive or negative?
7) In the calculation $7 - 12 + 8$, what should be carried out first: the addition or the subtraction?
8) When calculating $852 \div 3$ using short division, how would you record the result of dividing 8 by 3 in your working?
9) What is a multiple of a number?
10) In a factor tree for 140, the circled numbers are 7, 2, 5 and 2. What is the prime factorisation of 140?

Total:

Fractions

First Go:
..... /..... /.....

Simplifying Fractions

To simplify, divide top and bottom by the ______. Repeat until they won't divide any more.

÷5 ÷3
30/45 = 6/9 = .../......
÷5 ÷3
Top and bottom numbers of a simplified fraction have no ....

Mixed Numbers and Improper Fractions

MIXED NUMBER — has ______ part and ______ part, e.g. $2\frac{1}{3}$.

IMPROPER FRACTION — ______ is larger than ______, e.g. $\frac{7}{5}$.

To write mixed numbers as improper fractions:

1. Write as an ______.
2. Turn integer part into a ______.
3. ______ together.

$2\frac{3}{4} = 2 + \frac{3}{4} = \frac{......}{......} + \frac{3}{4} = \frac{......}{......}$ (1) (2) (3)

To write improper fractions as mixed numbers:

1. ______ top by bottom.
2. Answer is ______ part, ______ goes on top of fraction part.

(1) $17 \div 3 = 5$ remainder 2

(2) So $\frac{17}{3} = ...\frac{......}{......}$

Multiplying and Dividing

1. Rewrite any mixed numbers as ______.

If multiplying ↓ — If dividing: Turn 2nd fraction ______. Change ÷ to ×.

2. ______ tops and bottoms separately.
3. Simplify using ______ factors.

You can .... before doing the multiplications to make things easier.

$1\frac{3}{5} \times \frac{3}{10} = \frac{8}{5} \times \frac{3}{10}$ (1)

$= \frac{8 \times 3}{5 \times 10}$ (2)

$= \frac{......}{......} = \frac{......}{......}$ (3)

$\frac{7}{6} \div \frac{8}{3} = \frac{7}{6} \times \frac{3}{8}$ (1)

$= \frac{7 \times 3}{6 \times 8}$ (2)

$= \frac{......}{......} = \frac{......}{......}$ (3)

Ordering Fractions

COMMON DENOMINATOR — a number that all ______ divide into.

1. Rewrite the fractions with a ______.
2. Compare the ______ numbers.

EXAMPLE

Put $\frac{11}{6}$, $\frac{17}{12}$ and $\frac{7}{4}$ in descending order.

LCM of 6, 12, 4 is 12.

(1) $\frac{11}{6} = \frac{22}{12}$ $\frac{7}{4} = \frac{21}{12}$

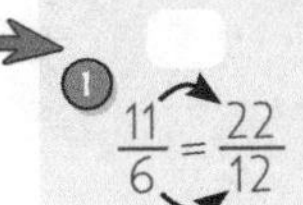

(2) $\frac{22}{12} > \frac{21}{12} > \frac{17}{12}$

So ______, ______, ______

Second Go: ...../...../.....

Fractions

Simplifying Fractions

To simplify, divide by the . Repeat until they .

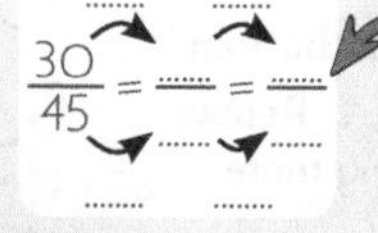

$\frac{30}{45} = \frac{\ldots}{\ldots} = \frac{\ldots}{\ldots}$

.... numbers of a simplified fraction have ....

Mixed Numbers and Improper Fractions

MIXED NUMBER — has , e.g. $2\frac{1}{3}$.

IMPROPER FRACTION — , e.g. $\frac{7}{5}$.

To write mixed numbers as improper fractions:

1 Write as 2 Turn 3

$2\frac{3}{4} =$ 1 = 2 = 3

To write improper fractions as mixed numbers:

1 2 Answer is

1 $17 \div 3 =$

2 So $\frac{17}{3} =$

Multiplying and Dividing

1 Rewrite any

If dividing

If multiplying

Turn

Change

2 Multiply

3 Simplify

You can .... to make things easier.

$1\frac{3}{5} \times \frac{3}{10} =$ 1

= 2

= = 3

$\frac{7}{6} \div \frac{8}{3} =$ 1

= 2

= = 3

Ordering Fractions

COMMON DENOMINATOR — a number that .

1 Rewrite the

2 Compare the

EXAMPLE

Put $\frac{11}{6}$, $\frac{17}{12}$ and $\frac{7}{4}$ in descending order.

LCM of 6, 12, 4 is 12.

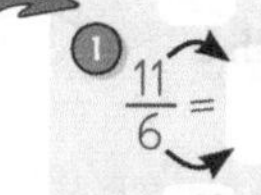

1 $\frac{11}{6} =$

$\frac{7}{4} =$

2 > >

So , ,

Fractions, Decimals and Percentages

First Go: ..... / ..... / .....

Adding and Subtracting Fractions

1. Make the same.
2. Add/subtract the numbers only.

EXAMPLE

Find $1\frac{1}{3} - \frac{5}{8}$.

① $1\frac{1}{3} - \frac{5}{8} = \quad - \frac{5}{8} = \frac{32}{24} - \frac{15}{24}$

Rewrite any mixed numbers.

② $= \frac{32 - 15}{24} =$

Finding Fractions of Amounts

1. Divide it by the .
2. Multiply by the .

.... then .... if it's easier.

$\frac{7}{12}$ of 240 = (240 ÷ ....) × 7

② = 20 × 7 = ...

Expressing as a Fraction

1. Write number over .
2. Cancel down.

210 as a fraction of 75

① $\frac{210}{75}$ = $\frac{.......}{.......}$ = $\frac{.......}{.......}$

② ÷3, ÷5

Common Conversions

Fraction	Decimal	Percentage
	0.5	50%
$\frac{1}{4}$		25%
$\frac{3}{4}$	0.75	
$\frac{1}{3}$		$33\frac{1}{3}$%
	0.6666...	$66\frac{2}{3}$%

Fraction	Decimal	Percentage
$\frac{1}{10}$	0.1	
$\frac{1}{5}$		20%
$\frac{1}{8}$	0.125	
	0.375	37.5%
$\frac{5}{2}$		250%

How to Convert

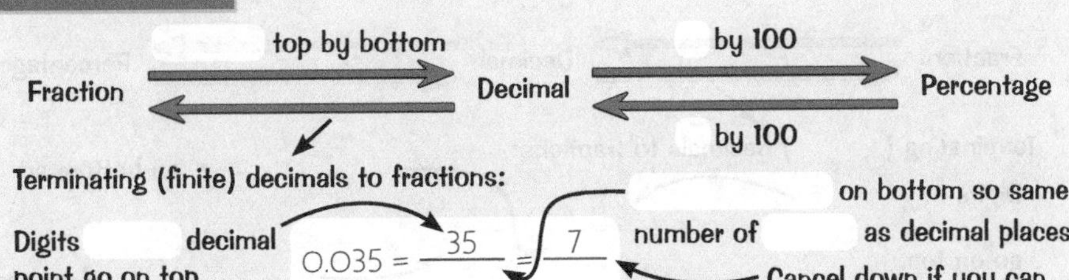

top by bottom
Fraction
Decimal
by 100
by 100
Percentage
Terminating (finite) decimals to fractions:
Digits decimal point go on top.
0.035 = 35/.......... = 7/..........
on bottom so same number of as decimal places.
Cancel down if you can.

Second Go: ...../...../.....

Fractions, Decimals and Percentages

Adding and Subtracting Fractions

1. Make
2. Add/subtract the

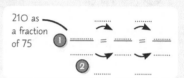

EXAMPLE

Find $1\frac{1}{3} - \frac{5}{8}$.

① $1\frac{1}{3} - \frac{5}{8} =$ $- \frac{5}{8} =$ $-$

Rewrite any mixed numbers.

② $=$ $=$

Finding Fractions of Amounts

1. Divide
2. Multiply

.... if it's easier.

$\frac{7}{12}$ of 240 = ...

= .... = ...

Expressing as a Fraction

1. Write
2.

210 as a fraction of 75

① .... = ... = ...

② ....

Common Conversions

Fraction	Decimal	Percentage
	0.5	
$\frac{1}{4}$		
		75%
		$33\frac{1}{3}\%$
$\frac{2}{3}$		

Fraction	Decimal	Percentage
		10%
$\frac{1}{5}$		
	0.125	
$\frac{3}{8}$		
	2.5	

How to Convert

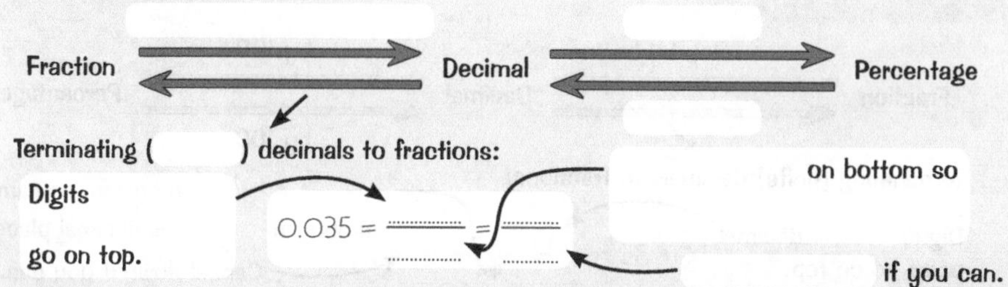

Rounding Numbers

First Go: ..... / ..... / .....

Two Steps to Round to Decimal Places

1. Identify the position of the digit in the rounded number.
2. Look at the digit to the — the decider.
   - If the decider is , round up the last digit.
   - If the decider is , leave the last digit as it is.

To round up a 9, replace it with ..... and add ..... to the digit on the ....

EXAMPLE

Round 8.6351 to 2 decimal places.

1. 8.6(3)51 — Circle the last digit.
2. The decider is , so the last digit rounds up to .
   8.6351 = (2 d.p.)

Three Steps to Round to Significant Figures

The 1st significant figure (s.f.) is the first digit that isn't . Each digit it (including zeros) is another significant figure.

1. Identify the position of the digit in the rounded number.
2. Look at the digit to the — the decider.
   - If the decider is , round up the last digit.
   - If the decider is , leave the last digit as it is.
3. Fill spaces the decimal point with zeros.

EXAMPLE

Round 732.5 to 1 significant figure.

1. (7)32.5 — Circle the last digit.
2. The decider is , so the stays as it is.
3. 732.5 = (1 s.f.)
   Fill 2 spaces with zeros.

Three Steps to Round to the Nearest...

... whole number, ten, hundred, etc.

1. Identify the position of the digit in the rounded number. (Units place, tens place, etc.)
2. Look at the digit to the — the decider.
   - If the decider is , round up the last digit.
   - If the decider is , leave the last digit as it is.
3. Fill spaces the decimal point with zeros.

EXAMPLE

Round 347 to the nearest ten.

1. 3(4)7 — Circle the last digit.
2. The decider is , so the last digit rounds up to .
3. 347 = (to nearest 10)
   Fill space with zero.

Second Go:
...../...../.....

Rounding Numbers

Two Steps to Round to Decimal Places

1. Identify the position of the .
2. Look at the — the decider.
   - If the decider is
   - If the decider is

To round up a 9,

....

....

....

EXAMPLE

Round 8.6351 to 2 decimal places.

1. 8 . 6 3 5 1 — Circle the last digit.
2. The decider is , so the last digit .

8.6351 = (2 d.p.)

Three Steps to Round to Significant Figures

The 1st significant figure (s.f.) is the . Each is another significant figure.

1. Identify the position of the .
2. Look at the — the decider.
   - If the decider is
   - If the decider is
3. Fill spaces with .

EXAMPLE

Round 732.5 to 1 significant figure.

1. 7 3 2 . 5 — Circle the last digit.
2. The decider is , so the last digit .
3. 732.5 = (1 s.f.)

Fill 2 spaces with zeros.

Three Steps to Round to the Nearest...

... whole number, ten, hundred, etc.

1. Identify the position of the .
2. Look at the — the decider.
   - If the decider is
   - If the decider is
3. Fill spaces with .

EXAMPLE

Round 347 to the nearest ten.

1. 3 4 7 — Circle the last digit.
2. The decider is , so the last digit .
3. 347 = (to nearest 10) — Fill space with zero.

Estimating and Rounding Errors

First Go: ..... /..... /.....

Estimating Calculations

1. Round numbers to or .
2. Work out answer using numbers.
3. If you're asked, say whether your value is an or .

EXAMPLE

Estimate the value of $\frac{18 + 7.6}{4.2}$. Is this an underestimate or overestimate?

$\frac{18 + 7.6}{4.2} \approx \frac{\quad + \quad}{\quad} = \frac{28}{4} =$ ①②

≈ means 'approximately ....'

③ The top numbers round and the bottom number rounds . The number being divided is and the number it's being divided by is smaller, so it's an .

Rounded Measurements

The actual value can be bigger or smaller than the rounded value by up to .

Minimum value: Rounded value −

Maximum value: Rounded value +

ERROR INTERVAL — range of values the actual value could have taken :

value ≤ Actual value < value

'≤' means the actual value could be .... to the .... value.

EXAMPLE

The volume of water in a jug is 430 ml to the nearest 10 ml. Find the error interval that contains the actual volume, v.

Minimum volume = 430 − = ml

Maximum volume = 430 + = ml

Error interval is ml ≤ v < ml

Truncated Measurements

TRUNCATING — chopping off .
E.g. 1.283 truncated to 1 d.p. = .

The actual value can be up to a bigger, but no than the truncated value.

Minimum value: Truncated value

Maximum value: Truncated value +

ERROR INTERVAL — range of values the actual value could have taken being truncated:

value ≤ Actual value < value

EXAMPLE

Give the error interval for a number, x, that is 5.23 truncated to 2 d.p.

Min value =

Max value = 5.23 + =

Digit in 2nd d.p. increases by 1.

Interval is ≤ x <

Second Go:
..... /..... /.....

Estimating and Rounding Errors

Estimating Calculations

1. Round
2. Work out
3. If you're asked, say whether

EXAMPLE

Estimate the value of $\frac{18 + 7.6}{4.2}$.
Is this an underestimate or overestimate?

$\frac{18 + 7.6}{4.2} \approx$ ① = ② =

≈ means ....

③ The top numbers and the bottom number .
The number being divided is bigger and the number so it's an .

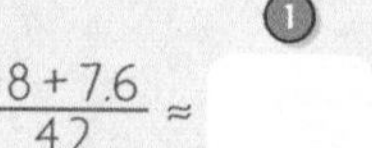

Rounded Measurements

The can be bigger or smaller than the by .

Minimum value: Rounded value

Maximum value: Rounded value

ERROR INTERVAL — range of values the :

value ≤ value < value

EXAMPLE

The volume of water in a jug is 430 ml to the nearest 10 ml. Find the error interval that contains the actual volume, v.

Minimum volume
= =

Maximum volume
= =

Error interval is

'≤' means the actual value ....

Truncated Measurements

TRUNCATING — . E.g. 1.283 truncated to 1 d.p. = .

The actual value can be , but than the truncated value.

Minimum value:

Maximum value: Truncated value

ERROR INTERVAL — range of values the :

value ≤ value < value

EXAMPLE

Give the error interval for a number, x, that is 5.23 truncated to 2 d.p.

Min value =

Max value =
=

(Digit in 2nd d.p. increases by 1.)

Interval is

Powers and Roots

First Go: ..... /..... /.....

Four Rules for Powers

POWERS — numbers multiplied by . → 3^4 = ... × .... × .... × ....

1. Powers of ten — the power tells you how many . 10^3 = ... (Power of 3)
2. Anything to the power 1 is . 8^1 = ...
3. Anything to the power is 1. $12^{....}$ = 1
4. 1 to any power is . 1^{27} = ...

Use a button on your .... to work out powers — it may look like $x^{\blacksquare}$ or y^x.

Five Rules for Calculations with Powers

These are only true for powers of the ....

1. Multiplying — .... the powers. $7^2 \times 7^4 = 7^{2+4} = 7^{....}$
2. Dividing — .... the powers. $5^6 \div 5^3 = 5^{6-3} = 5^{....}$
3. Raising one power to another — .... the powers. $(2^3)^2 = 2^{3 \times 2} = 2^{....}$
4. .... — apply power to TOP and BOTTOM. $\left(\frac{1}{4}\right)^2 = \frac{1^2}{4^2} = \frac{......}{......}$
5. Negative powers — turn .... and make power ....

$5^{-3} = \frac{1}{5^3} = \frac{......}{......}$

Square Roots

The square root ($\sqrt{\ }$) of a number multiplies by to give that number.
E.g. 4 × 4 = 16, so $\sqrt{16}$ = .
Find square roots using what you know about numbers, or your calculator.
You can also find the negative square root. It's the '–' version of the one.

EXAMPLE

Find both square roots of 81. (81 is a square number.)

81 = ... × ...., so positive square root = ...
and negative square root = ...

Cube Roots

The cube root ($\sqrt[3]{\ }$) of a number multiplies by to give that number.
E.g. 3 × 3 × 3 = 27, so $\sqrt[3]{27}$ = .
Find cube roots using what you know about numbers, or your calculator.

EXAMPLE

What is $\sqrt[3]{125}$? (125 is a cube number.)

125 = ... × .... × ....,
so $\sqrt[3]{125}$ = ...

Second Go:
...... /...... /......

Powers and Roots

Four Rules for Powers

Three to the power 4

POWERS — . ... = ...

1. **Powers of ten — the power tells you** . 10^3 = ... (Power of 3)
2. **Anything to the power is** . $8^{...}$ = ...
3. **to the power 0 is** . 12^0 = ...
4. **1 to power is** . 1^{27} = ...

Use a button on your .... to work out .... — it may look like $x^\blacksquare$ or y^x.

Five Rules for Calculations with Powers

These are only true for ....
....

1. **Multiplying —** ....
   $7^2 \times 7^4$ = ... = ...
2. **Dividing —** ....
   $5^6 \div 5^3$ = ... = ...
3. .... **one power to another —** ....
   $(2^3)^2$ = ... = ...
4. **Fractions —** ....
   $\left(\frac{1}{4}\right)^2 = \frac{......}{......} = \frac{......}{......}$
5. **Negative powers —** .... **and** ....
   $5^{-3} = \frac{......}{......} = \frac{......}{......}$

Square Roots

The square root ($\sqrt{\ }$) of a number

E.g. = 16, so $\sqrt{16}$ =

Find square roots using what you know about , or your .

You can also find the square root. It's the ' ' version of the one.

EXAMPLE

Find both square roots of 81. (81 is a square number.)

81 = ..., so .... square root = ...
and .... square root = ...

Cube Roots

The cube root ($\sqrt[3]{\ }$) of a number

E.g. = 27, so $\sqrt[3]{27}$ =

Find cube roots using what you know about , or your .

EXAMPLE

What is $\sqrt[3]{125}$? (125 is a cube number.)

125 = ...,
so $\sqrt[3]{125}$ = ...

Standard Form

First Go: ..... /..... /.....

Numbers in Standard Form

STANDARD FORM — used to write very ______ or very ______ numbers.

Number between ______ and ______ → $A \times 10^n$ ← **Number of places the ______ moves — ______ for big numbers, ______ for small numbers**

EXAMPLE

What is 24 300 in standard form?

24 300.0 — Count how far the decimal point moves to get 2.43

$= 2.43 \times 10^{....}$ — Big number, so positive n.

EXAMPLE

Express 3.81×10^{-5} as an ordinary number.

000003.81×10^{-5} — Negative n, so small number. Move the decimal point by this many places.

= ....

Three Steps to Multiply or Divide

1. ______ so the front numbers and powers of 10 are together.
2. Multiply/divide the front numbers. Use ______ to multiply/divide the powers of 10.
3. Put the answer in ______.

EXAMPLE

Find $(8 \times 10^2) \times (4 \times 10^3)$. Give your answer in standard form.

$(8 \times 10^2) \times (4 \times 10^3)$

1. $= (\quad \times \quad) \times (10^2 \times 10^3)$
2. $= 32 \times 10^{2+3}$ — Add powers

   $=$ ______ — Not in standard form — 32 isn't between 1 and 10.
3. $= 3.2 \times 10 \times 10^5$

   $=$ ______

Three Steps to Add or Subtract

1. Make sure the ______ ______ are the same.
2. Add/subtract ______.

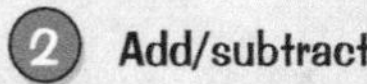

3. Put the answer in ______ if needed.

EXAMPLE

Find $(9.4 \times 10^7) + (6.7 \times 10^6)$. Give your answer in standard form.

$(9.4 \times 10^7) + (6.7 \times 10^6)$ — Different powers

1. $= (9.4 \times 10^7) + ($ ______ $\times 10 \times 10^6)$
2. $= ($ ______ $+$ ______ $) \times 10^7$

   $=$ ______ $\times 10^7$ — Not in standard form yet.
3. $=$ ______ $\times 10 \times 10^7$

   $=$ ______

Second Go:
...../...../.....

Standard Form

Numbers in Standard Form

STANDARD FORM — used to write .

Number  Number — positive for

EXAMPLE

What is 24 300 in standard form?

2 4 3 0 0 . 0

= ....

EXAMPLE

Express 3.81×10^{-5} as an ordinary number.

0 0 0 0 0 3 . 8 1 × 10^{-5}

= ....

Three Steps to Multiply or Divide

1. Rearrange so
2. Multiply/divide
   Use
3. Put

EXAMPLE

Find $(8 \times 10^2) \times (4 \times 10^3)$.
Give your answer in standard form.

$(8 \times 10^2) \times (4 \times 10^3)$

① = ×

② = × 10

= × 10

③ =

=

Three Steps to Add or Subtract

1. Make sure
2. Add/subtract
3. Put
   if needed.

EXAMPLE

Find $(9.4 \times 10^7) + (6.7 \times 10^6)$.
Give your answer in standard form.

$(9.4 \times 10^7) + (6.7 \times 10^6)$

① $= (9.4 \times 10^7) +$

② = × 10

= × 10

③ =

=

Mixed Practice Quizzes

What better way to round off everything you've learnt on p.15-26 than with a few quizzes. Find out if you've gained some superpowers (or are just super at powers).

Quiz 1

Date: ...... / ...... / ......

1) How do you simplify a fraction?
2) When rounding a number, which digit is the 'decider' and what does it tell you?
3) What is the value of 1^{18}?
4) What is the first step in multiplying two mixed numbers?
5) Which digit in 0.1035 is the second significant figure?
6) What would be the first step in multiplying two numbers in standard form?
7) What is the first thing you need to do to add $\frac{3}{8}$ and $\frac{1}{6}$?
8) What number goes on top when 0.53 is converted to a fraction?
9) What is meant by the error interval when a number has been rounded?
10) How do you raise a fraction to a power?

Total:

Quiz 2

Date: ...... / ...... / ......

1) What is a common denominator?
2) What is the first step when rounding a number?
3) True or false? A fraction is in its simplest form if the numbers on the top and bottom of the fraction have no common factors.
4) What is the value of 5^0?
5) What is the symbol for 'approximately equal to'?
6) What do you need to do to write one number as a fraction of another?
7) What is 20% as a decimal?
8) Is 12×10^4 in standard form?
9) A length is rounded to the nearest centimetre. Up to how much bigger could the actual value be than the rounded value?
10) What are the positive and negative square roots of 36?

Total:

Mixed Practice Quizzes

Quiz 3

Date: ...... / ...... / ......

1) How do you divide two powers of the same number?
2) What is meant by truncating a number?
3) How do you convert a mixed number into an improper fraction?
4) What is the first thing you should do to order fractions?
5) How do you estimate the answer to a calculation?
6) How do you convert a decimal to a percentage?
7) True or false? If the 'decider' is 5, the last digit in the rounded number stays as it is.
8) If a number is in standard form, between which two values should its first number be?
9) What is the first step in multiplying two improper fractions?
10) What do you need to do to the powers to work out $(8^2)^4$?

Total:

Quiz 4

Date: ...... / ...... / ......

1) What do you need to do to convert a fraction into a decimal?
2) What is the integer part when $\frac{28}{3}$ is converted into a mixed number?
3) How do you multiply two powers of the same number?
4) What is the first significant figure of a number?
5) What do you do when dividing fractions that you wouldn't do when multiplying them?
6) To calculate $(1.2 \times 10^3) + (5.8 \times 10^3)$, what do you need to do with the front numbers?
7) How do you find a fraction of a number?
8) What is 13.685 rounded to 1 decimal place?
9) 16.2×7.7 is estimated by calculating 20×8. Will this be an underestimate or overestimate?
10) When a number is truncated to 1 decimal place, its value is 143.2. What is the minimum value of the original number?

Total:

Algebra Basics

First Go: ..... /..... /.....

Collecting Like Terms

TERM — a collection of numbers, and , all multiplied/divided together.

Three steps to collect like terms when you have a mixture of different terms:

1. Put around each term.
2. Move so like terms are grouped .
3. like terms.

EXAMPLE

Simplify:

a) $2x + 5x - 3x$ — All x terms, so just combine.

$2x + 5x - 3x =$

b) $7a + 2 - 3a + 5$ — Include the +/– sign in each bubble.

1. $7a$ $+2$ $-3a$ $+5$
2. $= 7a$ $-3a$ $+2$ $+5$
3. $=$

Using Letters

Notation	Meaning
abc	a b c
	5 × a
$3\sqrt{a}$	3 $\sqrt{a}$
y	y × y × y × y
pq^2	p × ×
$(mn)^2$	m × m × ×
$\frac{a}{b}$	a b

The signs are left out.

Only q is — not p.

Use power rules to divide powers of the ....

Powers tell you how many letters are together.

Brackets mean both m and n are .

Multiplying Brackets

Multiply each term the bracket by the bit the bracket.

Three steps to multiply brackets:

1. each bracket separately.
2. Group together.
3. the expression.

EXAMPLE

Expand $3x(2x + 1) + 4(3 - 5x)$.

1. $3x(2x + 1) + 4(3 - 5x)$
   $= (3x \times 2x) + (\quad)$
   $+ (4 \times 3) + (\quad)$
   $= 6x^2 + \quad + 12 -$
2. $= 6x^2 + \quad - \quad + 12$
3. $=$

Second Go:
...../...../.....

Algebra Basics

Collecting Like Terms

TERM — a collection of

Three steps to collect like terms when you have a mixture of different terms:

1. Put bubbles
2. Move bubbles
3.

EXAMPLE

Simplify:

a) $2x + 5x - 3x$ — All x terms, so just combine.

$2x + 5x - 3x =$

b) $7a + 2 - 3a + 5$

Include the +/– sign in each bubble.

1.
2. =
3. =

Using Letters

Notation	Meaning
	a × b × c
	5 × a
$3\sqrt{a}$	
y^4	
pq^2	
$(mn)^2$	
	a ÷ b

The signs are

Only

— not p.

Use .... to divide ....

Powers tell you

Brackets mean

Multiplying Brackets

Multiply

by

Three steps to multiply brackets:

1. Expand .
2. Group .
3. Simplify .

EXAMPLE

Expand $3x(2x + 1) + 4(3 - 5x)$.

1. $3x(2x + 1) + 4(3 - 5x)$

$= (\quad) + (\quad)$

$+ (\quad) + (\quad)$

$=$

2. =
3. =

Double Brackets and Factorising

First Go: ..... /..... /.....

Using the FOIL Method

To multiply out   brackets:

- Multiply .... terms of each bracket.
- Multiply .... terms together.
- Multiply .... terms together.
- Multiply .... terms of each bracket.

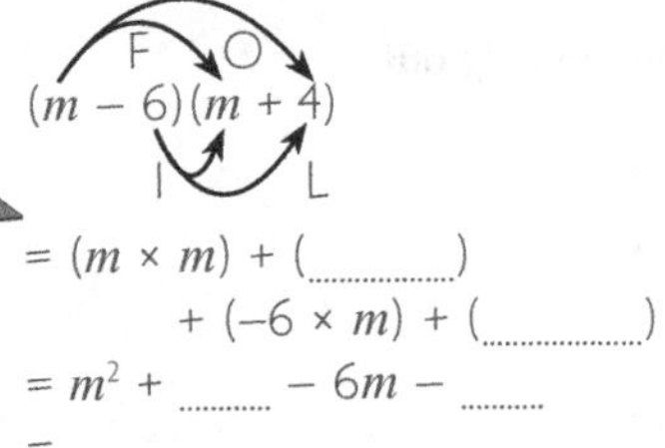

$= (m \times m) + (\text{.........})$
$+ (-6 \times m) + (\text{.........})$
$= m^2 + \text{......} - 6m - \text{......}$
$= \text{..................}$

To multiply squared brackets, write them out as   , then use the FOIL method as normal.

EXAMPLE

Expand and simplify $(2x - 5)^2$.

$(2x - 5)(2x - 5)$

$= (\text{.........}) + (2x \times -5) + (\text{.........}) + (-5 \times -5)$

$= \text{......} - 10x - \text{......} + 25 = \text{..................}$

Factorising Expressions

FACTORISING — putting   back in.

1. Take out the   that goes into all terms.
2. Take out the   of each letter that goes into all terms.
3. Open bracket and   what's needed to reproduce the   terms.
4. Check your answer by   the bracket.

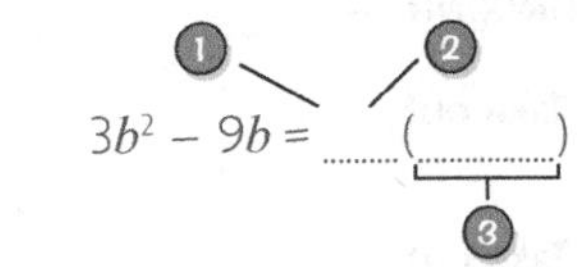

4 .... $= 3b \times b + 3b \times -3$
$= 3b^2 - 9b$

The bits put in front of the bracket are the ....

The Difference of Two Squares (D.O.T.S.)

D.O.T.S. — 'one thing squared' take away '   '.

Use this rule for factorising: $a^2 - b^2 = (\text{.........})(\text{.........})$

EXAMPLE

Factorise $x^2 - 25$.

$x^2 - 25 = (x \text{ ......})(x \text{ ......})$

EXAMPLE

Factorise $4p^2 - 9q^2$.

$4p^2 - 9q^2 = (2p \text{ ......})(2p \text{ ......})$

Second Go: ...../...../.....

Double Brackets and Factorising

Using the FOIL Method

To multiply out ______ :

-
-
-
-

F O
$(m - 6)(m + 4)$
I L

$= (\ldots) + (\ldots)$
$+ (\ldots) + (\ldots)$
$= \ldots$
$= \ldots$

To multiply squared brackets, write them out as ______ , then use the ______ as normal.

EXAMPLE

Expand and simplify $(2x - 5)^2$.

$(2x - 5)(2x - 5)$

$= (\ldots) + (\ldots) + (\ldots) + (\ldots)$

$= \ldots = \ldots$

Factorising Expressions

FACTORISING — ______ .

1. Take out
2. Take out
3. Open bracket and
4. Check your answer by

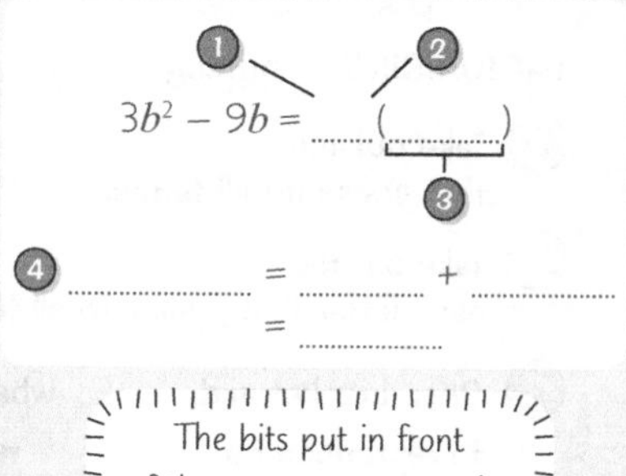

The bits put in front of the ______ are the ______.

The Difference of Two Squares (D.O.T.S.)

D.O.T.S. — ______ .

Use this rule for factorising: ______

EXAMPLE

Factorise $x^2 - 25$.

$x^2 - 25 = \ldots$

EXAMPLE

Factorise $4p^2 - 9q^2$.

$4p^2 - 9q^2 = \ldots$

Solving Equations

First Go: ..... /..... /.....

Three Rules for Rearranging Equations

1. Do the to both sides of the equation.
2. Do the to get rid of things you don't want.

   ...... is the opposite of −
   ...... is the opposite of ÷
3. Keep going until you have a letter .

EXAMPLE

Solve $x - 4 = 9$.

① $x - 4 + 4 = 9 + 4$ — ② The opposite of '−4' is '+4'.

③ $x =$ ....

EXAMPLE

Solve $3x = 21$.

① $3x \div 3 = 21 \div 3$ — ② $3x$ means $3 \times x$ — so do the opposite, which is '÷3'.

③ $x =$ ....

Two-Step Equations

If there's an x term and a number on the same side of the equation:

1. Add/subtract the .
2. Multiply/divide to get ' '.

EXAMPLE

Solve $5x - 3 = 27$.

① $5x - 3 + 3 = 27 + 3$ — Add 3 to both sides.

$5x =$ ....

② $5x \div 5 = 30 \div 5$ — Divide both sides by 5.

$x =$ ....

When x is on Both Sides

1. Get all the on one side of =, and all the on the other.
2. Multiply/divide to get ' '.

EXAMPLE

Solve $5x + 8 = 2x - 7$.

① $5x + 8 - 8 = 2x - 7 - 8$

$5x =$ ....

$5x - 2x =$ ....

.... $= -15$

② $3x \div 3 = -15 \div 3$

$x =$ ....

Equations with Brackets

1. Multiply out the .
2. Get all the on one side of =, and all the on the other.
3. Multiply/divide to get ' '.

EXAMPLE

Solve $2(4x + 1) = 5x + 11$.

① $= 5x + 11$

② $- 5x = 5x + 11 - 5x$

$= 11$

$3x + 2 - 2 = 11 - 2$

③ $3x =$

$x =$

Second Go:
...../...../.....

Solving Equations

Three Rules for Rearranging Equations

1. Do the same thing

2. Do the opposite operation

+ is the ....

× is the ....

3. Keep going until

EXAMPLE

Solve $x - 4 = 9$.

① $x - 4$ .... $= 9$ .... ②

③ $x =$ ....

EXAMPLE

Solve $3x = 21$.

① $3x$ .... $= 21$ .... ②

③ $x =$ ....

Two-Step Equations

If there's an x term and a number on the of the equation:

the number.

2. to get 'x = ...'.

EXAMPLE

Solve $5x - 3 = 27$.

① $5x - 3$ .... $= 27$ ....

.... = ...

② .... = ...

$x =$ ....

When x is on Both Sides

1. Get all the
and all the

2. to get 'x = ...'.

EXAMPLE

Solve $5x + 8 = 2x - 7$.

① $5x + 8$ .... $= 2x - 7$ ....

$5x =$ ....

.... = ...

.... = ...

② .... = ...

$x =$ ....

Equations with Brackets

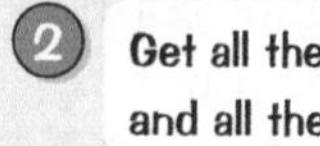

to get 'x = ...'.

EXAMPLE

Solve $2(4x + 1) = 5x + 11$.

① $= 5x + 11$

② =

$= 11$

$3x + 2 =$

③ $3x =$

=

Expressions, Formulas and Functions

First Go: ..... /..... /.....

Definitions

EXPRESSION	A collection of — they don't have an .	$4x + 5$
EQUATION	An that has an in it.	$3x - 2 = 7$
FORMULA	A that helps you work something out (has an).	$F = \frac{9}{5}C + 32$
FUNCTION	An that takes an , processes it and produces an .	'Multiply by 6, then subtract 3'

Putting Numbers into Formulas

1. Write out the .
2. Write it out again, but into the right-hand side.
3. Work it out in .

EXAMPLE

The formula for the cost, £C, of hiring a village hall for h hours is £$C = 25h + 100$. Find the cost of hiring the hall for 4 hours.

1. £$C = 25h + 100$
2. £$C = 25 \times$ $+ 100$
3. £$C =$ $+ 100 =$

Use BODMAS to work it out in the right order.

So it costs £ for 4 hours.

Function Machines

Put in a number and .... to get the output.

If you know the output, you can use the function machine .... to find the input.

EXAMPLE

This function machine represents the function "multiply by 3 and subtract 2".

$x \rightarrow$ [×3] $\rightarrow$ [−2] $\rightarrow y$

a) Find y when $x = 3$.

3 → (×3) → (−2) →

b) Find x when $y = 13$.

13 → (+2) → (÷3) →

Work backwards through the function machine and reverse every step.

Second Go:
..... /..... /.....

Expressions, Formulas and Functions

Definitions

EXPRESSION		$4x + 5$
EQUATION		$3x - 2 = 7$
FORMULA		$F = \frac{9}{5}C + 32$
FUNCTION		'Multiply by 6, then subtract 3'

Putting Numbers into Formulas

1. Write
2. Write it out again, but
3.

EXAMPLE

The formula for the cost, £*C*, of hiring a village hall for *h* hours is £$C = 25h + 100$. Find the cost of hiring the hall for 4 hours.

1. £C =
2. £C =
3. £C = =

Use BODMAS to work it out in the right order.

So it costs .

Function Machines

Put in a number and ....

If you know the ...., you can use the function machine

....

EXAMPLE

This function machine represents the function "multiply by 3 and subtract 2".

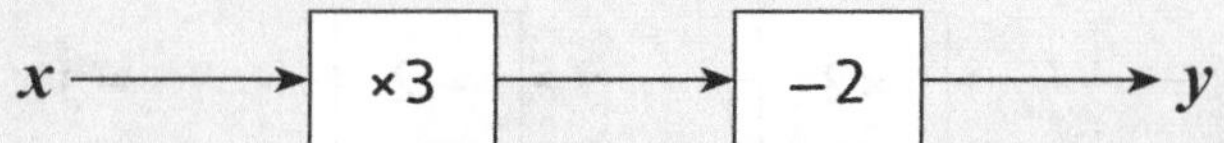

a) Find y when $x = 3$.

3 ⟶ ⟶

b) Find x when $y = 13$.

13 ⟶ ⟶

Using Formulas and Expressions

First Go: ..... /..... /.....

Making Expressions

1. Work out what the is.
2. Extract all the from the question.
3. Make an expression or .
4. Use the expression or formula to form an and solve to find the .

You won't always be asked to solve for the variable.

EXAMPLE

Abi, Padma and Carl hand out 64 flyers. Padma hands out twice as many as Abi, and Carl hands out 4 more than Padma. How many flyers does Abi hand out?

1. x = the number of flyers Abi hands out
2. Abi = x Padma = $2x$ Carl = $2x + 4$
3. Total = + + ( ) =
4. = 64

$5x = 60$, so $x =$

So Abi hands out .

Using Shape Properties

Follow the same steps as above. Use things like ...., areas or .... to form the expressions.

EXAMPLE

For the shapes below, the perimeter of the square is the same as the perimeter of the triangle. Find the value of x.

Triangle perimeter = $(4x + 1) + (2x + 3) + 2x =$

Square perimeter = $4(x + 5) =$

$8x + 4 = 4x + 20$ — The perimeters are the same, so form an equation and solve.

$4x =$

$x =$

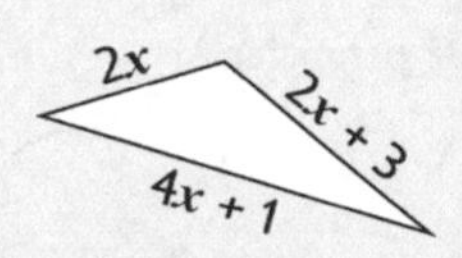

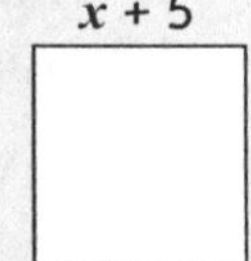

Three Rules for Rearranging Formulas

1. Do the to both sides of the formula.
2. Do the to get rid of things you don't want.

..... is the opposite of –
..... is the opposite of ÷

3. Keep going until you have the letter you want .

EXAMPLE

Rearrange $q = \frac{7p - 3}{5}$ to make p the subject of the formula.

1. $q \div 5 = \frac{7p - 3}{5} \div 5$

$5q =$

$5q + 3 = 7p - 3 + 3$ (2)

$5q + 3 =$

$(5q + 3) \div 7 = 7p \div 7$

3. $p =$

Second Go:
...../...../.....

Using Formulas and Expressions

Making Expressions

1. Work out
2. Extract
3. Make
4. Use the expression or formula to

You won't always be asked to solve for the variable.

EXAMPLE

Abi, Padma and Carl hand out 64 flyers. Padma hands out twice as many as Abi, and Carl hands out 4 more than Padma. How many flyers does Abi hand out?

1. $x =$
2. Abi = Padma = Carl =
3. Total = =
4.

$5x =$, so $x =$

So Abi hands out

Using Shape Properties

Follow the same steps as above. Use things like ....

.... to form the ....

EXAMPLE

For the shapes below, the perimeter of the square is the same as the perimeter of the triangle. Find the value of x.

Triangle perimeter = =

Square perimeter = =

=

$4x =$

$x =$

The perimeters are the same, so form an equation and solve.

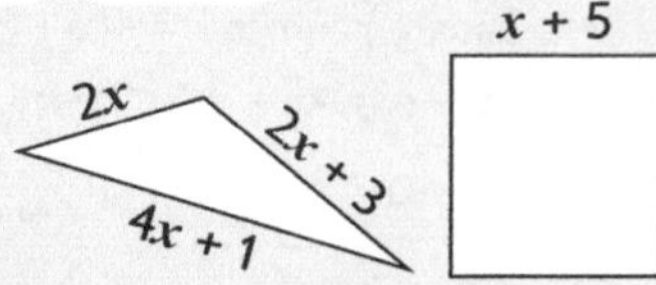

Three Rules for Rearranging Formulas

1. Do the same thing
2. Do the opposite operation

+ is the ....

× is the ....

3. Keep going until

EXAMPLE

Rearrange $q = \frac{7p - 3}{5}$ to make p the subject of the formula.

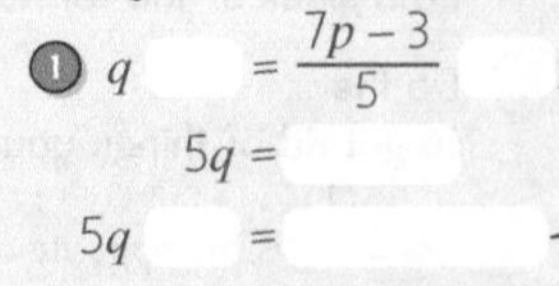

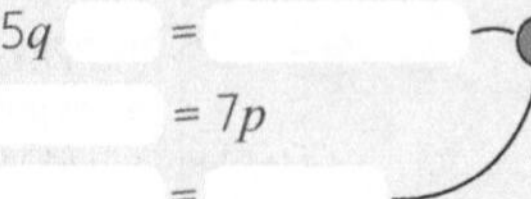

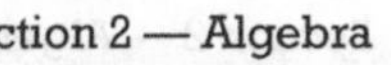

Mixed Practice Quizzes

Algebra can be tricky. The solution? Having a go at these quizzes, covering everything on p.29-38. Mark each test yourself and pop your score in the box.

Quiz 1

Date: ...... / ...... / ......

1) What is an equation?
2) True or false? $(2x + 3)^2 = 4x^2 + 9$.
3) What is the first step to solve equations that involve brackets?
4) What is the first thing you'd do to rearrange $x = 2y - 5$ to make y the subject?
5) What is a term?
6) What is the first step to make an expression from a wordy problem?
7) Multiply out $3(2x - 5)$.
8) What goes outside the bracket when factorising an expression?
9) A function machine takes a number, divides it by 3, then adds 4. What is the output when 9 is put into the machine?
10) What is the first step to collect like terms?

Total:

Quiz 2

Date: ...... / ...... / ......

1) How do you multiply out a single bracket?
2) What is $a \times a \times b \times b$ in its simplest form?
3) What is a formula?
4) Multiply out $(x + 3)(x - 1)$.
5) Harry is three years older than Wei. Poppy is twice as old as Wei. Give an expression for the sum of their ages.
6) True or false? When rearranging a formula, you should do the opposite thing to each side.
7) How do you find the value put into a function machine from the output?
8) How could you check that a factorisation is correct?
9) Solve $x + 8 = 5$.
10) What is the rule for factorising the difference of two squares?

Total:

Mixed Practice Quizzes

Quiz 3

Date: ...... / ...... / ......

1) What is an expression?
2) Collect like terms to simplify $2y + 9 - 6y - 4$.
3) What is the first thing you should do to multiply out squared brackets?
4) The formula to convert miles (m) into kilometres (k) is $k = 1.6m$. What is 10 miles in kilometres?
5) What is the first thing you'd do to solve $5x - 9 = 6$?
6) How would you write 8 lots of x multiplied together?
7) What would the x^2 term be when $x(4x - 1) - 3x(2x + 3)$ is multiplied out?
8) What is the first step you'd take to make b the subject of $a = \frac{5b - 2}{4}$?
9) Factorise $x^2 - 49$.
10) A function machine takes a number, multiplies it by 5, then subtracts 3. What was the input if the output is 17?

Total:

Quiz 4

Date: ...... / ...... / ......

1) Simplify $3 \times p \times p \times q$.
2) What is meant by factorising an expression?
3) What is the first step to solve equations that have x on both sides?
4) What term goes outside the brackets when $4x^2 + 6xy + 12xy^2$ is fully factorised?
5) Give the three rules for rearranging equations.
6) What is a function?
7) How do you show $x \div y$ in algebra notation?
8) Given the formula $m = 3n + 7$, find m when $n = 2$.
9) What do the letters of FOIL stand for?
10) A rectangle and a square have the same area. The rectangle has sides 4 cm and x cm long. The square has sides 6 cm long. Find x.

Total:

Sequences

First Go: ...../...../.....

Number and Shape Sequences

To find the rule for a sequence, work out how to get from to the .

LINEAR SEQUENCES — adding or subtracting the :

Rule: .... from the previous term

GEOMETRIC SEQUENCES — multiplying or dividing by the :

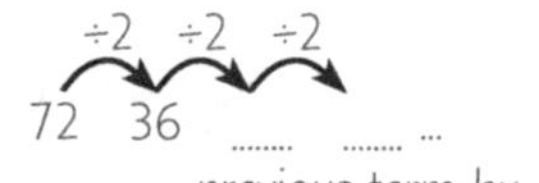

Rule: .... previous term by ....

Pattern 1 Pattern 2 Pattern 3

Rule: .... circles to previous pattern

Pattern 1 Pattern 2 Pattern 3

Rule: .... number of squares by ....

nth Term of Linear Sequences

NTH TERM — a rule that gives the in a sequence when you put in different .

1. Find the — this is what you multiply n by.
2. Work out what to .
3. Put together.

EXAMPLE

Find the nth term of the sequence 7, 11, 15, 19 ...

1. 11 − 7 = , 15 − 11 = , etc. So common difference =
2. For n = 1, 4n = 4. 7 − 4 = , so is added to each term.
3. So nth term is

Deciding if a Term is in a Sequence

Set nth term rule equal to the number and . The term is in the sequence if n is a .

EXAMPLE

Is 37 a term in the sequence with the nth term 6n − 1?

$6n - 1 = 37$

$6n =$ ....

$n = 6.333...$

So 37 .... in the sequence.

Other Types of Sequences

QUADRATIC SEQUENCE — the number you add/subtract by the each time.

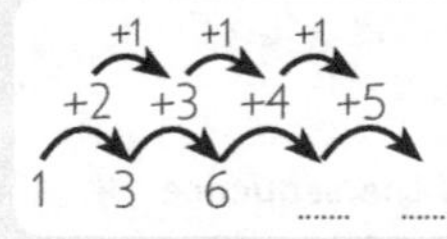

Terms in this sequence are the .... numbers.

FIBONACCI-TYPE SEQUENCE — previous two terms together.

4 + 6

2 4 6 ....

2 + 4 6 + 10

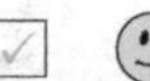   

Second Go:
...../...../.....

Sequences

Number and Shape Sequences

To find the for a sequence, work out how to get from .

LINEAR SEQUENCES —

31 24 ....

Rule: ....

Pattern 1 Pattern 2 Pattern 3

Rule: ....

....

GEOMETRIC SEQUENCES —

72 36 ....

Rule: ....

Pattern 1 Pattern 2 Pattern 3

Rule: ....

....

nth Term of Linear Sequences

NTH TERM — a rule that gives

1. **Find the —**
   this is what you .
2. **Work out .**
3. **Put .**

EXAMPLE

Find the nth term of the sequence 7, 11, 15, 19 ...

1. So common difference =
2. so is added to each term.
3. So nth term is

Deciding if a Term is in a Sequence

Set nth term rule . The term is in the sequence .

EXAMPLE

Is 37 a term in the sequence with the nth term 6n – 1?

6n – 1 = ...

6n = ...

n = ...

So ....

Other Types of Sequences

QUADRATIC SEQUENCE —

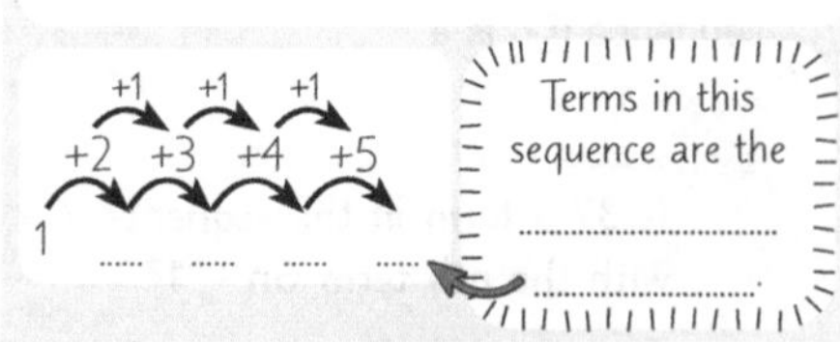

FIBONACCI-TYPE SEQUENCE —

Inequalities and Quadratic Equations

First Go: ..... /..... /.....

Solving Inequalities

...... means GREATER THAN

...... means LESS THAN

...... means GREATER THAN OR EQUAL TO

...... means LESS THAN OR EQUAL TO

To represent inequalities on number lines:

- Use a circle (●) for ≤ or ≥
- Use an circle (○) for < or >

Solve inequalities like equations — but if you multiply/divide by a , flip the inequality sign.

EXAMPLE

Show $-2 \le x < 5$ on the number line below.

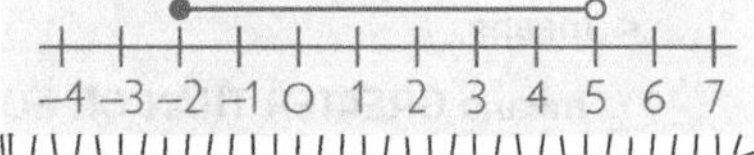

This inequality means "x is greater than or equal to .... and less than ....".

EXAMPLE

Solve $3 - 5x \le 18$.

$3 - 5x \le 18$

$-5x \le 18 - 3$

$-5x \le 15$

Divided by a negative number, so flip the sign.

Solving Quadratic Equations

Standard form of a quadratic equation:

...... + ... + ... = 0

(b and c can be any number)

To FACTORISE — put it into .

To SOLVE — find the that make each bracket .

Six steps to solve quadratics:

1. Rearrange to .
2. Write two brackets:
3. Find two numbers that to give 'c' AND to give 'b'.
4. Fill in signs.
5. Check by .
6. Solve the equation.

EXAMPLE

Solve $x^2 - 6x = -8$.

1. $x^2 - 6x + 8 = 0$
2. $(x \quad)(x \quad) = 0$
3. Factor pairs of 8: and
   $1 + 8 = 9$ and $8 - 1 = 7$
   $2 + 4 = 6$ and $4 - 2 = 2$
   So the numbers are 2 and 4.
4. $(x - 2)(x - 4) = 0$
5. $(x - 2)(x - 4)$
   $= x^2 - 4x - 2x + 8$
   $=$
6. $(x - 2) = 0 \Rightarrow$
   $(x - 4) = 0 \Rightarrow$

Work out which signs you need by looking at c. If c is ...., the signs will be the same. If c is ...., the signs will be different.

Second Go:
..... /..... /.....

Inequalities and Quadratic Equations

Solving Inequalities

> means ....

< means ....

...... means **GREATER THAN OR EQUAL TO**

...... means **LESS THAN OR EQUAL TO**

To represent inequalities on number lines:

- Use a (●) for
- Use an (○) for

Solve inequalities like equations — but if you .

EXAMPLE

Show $-2 \le x < 5$ on the number line below.

−4 −3 −2 −1 0 1 2 3 4 5 6 7

This inequality means "..............
....
...."

EXAMPLE

Solve $3 - 5x \le 18$.

$3 - 5x \le 18$

$\le$

$\le$

Divided by a negative number, so flip the sign.

Solving Quadratic Equations

Standard form of a quadratic equation:

(b and c can be any number)

To FACTORISE — .

To SOLVE — .

Six steps to solve quadratics:

1. Rearrange
2. Write
3. Find two numbers
4. Fill in
5. Check
6. Solve the equation.

EXAMPLE

Solve $x^2 - 6x = -8$.

1.
2.
3. Factor pairs of 8: .... and ....
   $1 + 8 =$ ..... and $8 - 1 =$ .....
   $2 + 4 =$ ..... and $4 - 2 =$ .....
   So the numbers are ....
4. (   )(   ) = 0
5. (   )(   )
   =
   =
6. = 0 ⇒
   = 0 ⇒

Work out which signs you need by looking at c. If c is positive, ... If c is negative, ...

Simultaneous Equations and Proof

First Go: ...../...../.....

Solving Simultaneous Equations

Six steps to solve them:

1. Rearrange into the form .
2. Match up the for one of the variables.
3. to get rid of a variable.
4. Solve the equation.
5. Substitute the value back into one of the equations.
6. your answer works.

EXAMPLE

Solve the simultaneous equations
$5 - 2x = 3y$ and $5x + 4 = -2y$

1. (1) ← Label your equations.
   (2)
2. (1) × 5: $10x + 15y = 25$ (3)
   (2) × 2: $10x + 4y = -8$ (4)
3. (3) – (4): — $25 - -8 = 33$
4. $11y = 33 \Rightarrow y =$
5. Sub $y = 3$ into (1): $2x + (3 \times 3) = 5$
   $\Rightarrow 2x = 5 - 9 \Rightarrow 2x = -4 \Rightarrow x =$
6. Sub x and y into (2):
   $(5 \times -2) + (2 \times 3) = -4$
   So the solution is , .

Proof

To show that something is , find an example that .

EXAMPLE

Find an example to show that this statement is false:
"The sum of two square numbers is always odd."

$1 + 4 = 5$ (.........) $4 + 9 = 13$ (.........) $1 + 9 = 10$ (.........), so the statement is ....

To show that something is , you might need to to show two things are the , or show something is a of a number.

EXAMPLE

Prove $(n - 4)^2 - (n + 1)^2 \equiv -5(2n - 3)$.

$(n - 4)^2 - (n + 1)^2$
$\equiv (n^2 - 8n + 16) - (n^2 + 2n + 1)$
$\equiv n^2 - 8n + 16 - n^2 - 2n - 1$
$\equiv$ ....
$\equiv$ ....

The identity symbol '$\equiv$' means this is true for ....

EXAMPLE

$y = 2(6x + 4) + 3(3x - 5) + 1$
Show y is a multiple of 3 when x is a whole number.

$y = 2(6x + 4) + 3(3x - 5) + 1$
$= 12x + 8 + 9x - 15 + 1$
$=$ .... $=$ ....

y can be written as ..... × something (where the something is ....), so it is a multiple of 3.

Second Go:
...../...../.....

Simultaneous Equations and Proof

Solving Simultaneous Equations

Six steps to solve them:

1. **Rearrange**
2. **Match up**
3. **Add or subtract**
4.
5. **Substitute**
6. **Check**

EXAMPLE

Solve the simultaneous equations
$5 - 2x = 3y$ and $5x + 4 = -2y$

1. (1) ← Label your equations.
   (2)
2. (1) × 5: (3)
   (2) × 2: (4)
3. (3) – (4):
4. ⇒
5. Sub into (1):
   ⇒ ⇒ ⇒
6. Sub x and y into (2):
   = =

So the solution is .

Proof

To show that something is , find an .

EXAMPLE

Find an example to show that this statement is false:
"The sum of two square numbers is always odd."

.... (odd) .... (odd) .... (even), so the statement is ....

To show that something is , you might need to , or show something .

EXAMPLE

Prove $(n-4)^2 - (n+1)^2 \equiv -5(2n-3)$.

$(n-4)^2 - (n+1)^2$
$\equiv ($ $) - ($ $)$
$\equiv$
$\equiv$
$\equiv$

The identity symbol '.....' means this is ....

EXAMPLE

$y = 2(6x + 4) + 3(3x - 5) + 1$
Show y is a multiple of 3 when x is a whole number.

$y = 2(6x + 4) + 3(3x - 5) + 1$
= + + 1
= =

y can be written as
(where the),
so it is a multiple of 3.

Mixed Practice Quizzes

Next in the sequence comes some quizzes to test how much you learned from p.41-46. Give it your best shot, then mark your answers to see how you did.

Quiz 1

Date: ...... / ...... / ......

1) What does the symbol ≥ mean?
2) How should you check your answer when solving simultaneous equations?
3) If a quadratic equation has a positive value for c, will the signs in the factorised equation be the same or different?
4) How do you find the next term in a Fibonacci-type sequence?
5) True or false? $x \leq 7$ means x is greater than or equal to 7.
6) What is the first thing you would do to solve the equations $3x - 4y = 2$ and $2x + 5y = 9$ simultaneously?
7) If you multiply or divide both sides by a negative number when solving an inequality, what happens to the inequality sign?
8) What is meant by the common difference of a linear sequence?
9) How can you prove that a statement is false?
10) Is 25 a term in the sequence $6n + 1$?

Total:

Quiz 2

Date: ...... / ...... / ......

1) What is the standard form for a quadratic equation?
2) How do you get from one number to the next in a geometric sequence?
3) True or false? When n is an integer, $9n + 6$ is always a multiple of 3.
4) Which two symbols are represented by an open circle on a number line?
5) What is the rule for the sequence 2, 6, 18, 54 ...?
6) How do you solve a factorised quadratic equation?
7) Prove this statement is false: "The product of two primes is always odd."
8) What is meant by the nth term of a linear sequence?
9) Factorise $x^2 - 6x + 8$.
10) What do you do with the value of the first variable to find the value of the second variable when solving simultaneous equations?

Total:

Mixed Practice Quizzes

Quiz 3

Date: ...... / ...... / ......

1) What does the symbol ≡ mean?
2) How do you get from one term to the next in a linear sequence?
3) How would you decide if a term is in a sequence?
4) What does the inequality $2 < x \leq 7$ mean?
5) How do you get rid of a variable when solving simultaneous equations?
6) How would you prove that two expressions are the same?
7) Find the possible values of x when $(x - 2)(x + 5) = 0$.
8) On a number line, are closed or open circles used to represent the symbols ≤ and ≥?
9) Rearrange $x^2 = 6 - 5x$ into the standard form of a quadratic equation.
10) What is the nth term of the sequence −1, 1, 3, 5 ...?

Total:

Quiz 4

Date: ...... / ...... / ......

1) What is the difference between linear sequences and quadratic sequences?
2) Solve the inequality $x + 4 > 10$.
3) What is meant by factorising a quadratic equation?
4) What type of sequence is 37, 26, 15, 4 ...?
5) What form should you rearrange equations into before solving them simultaneously?
6) List the whole numbers that satisfy the inequality $-4 \leq x < 1$.
7) If the signs are different in a factorised quadratic equation, will the value of c be positive or negative in the expanded equation?
8) Would the inequality $x \leq 5$ be represented by an open or closed circle on a number line?
9) Prove this statement is false: "The sum of two square numbers is never a square number."
10) What is the common difference in the sequence 11, 14, 17, 20 ...?

Total:

Coordinates and Straight Lines

First Go: ..... /..... /.....

Coordinates and Quadrants

Coordinates are written as: (......, ...)

is the horizontal axis

is the vertical axis

To read coordinates, go

(-coordinate then -coordinate).

The can be positive or negative, depending on which of the four (regions) you're in:

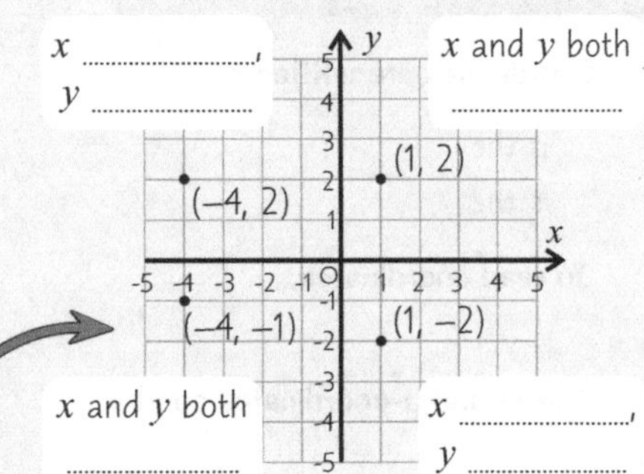

Midpoint of a Line

MIDPOINT OF A LINE SEGMENT — point exactly between the line's .

Three steps to find the midpoint:

1. Find the of the x-coordinates.
2. Find the of the y-coordinates.
3. Put them in .

EXAMPLE

Point A has coordinates (–8, 2) and Point B has coordinates (6, 10). Find the coordinates of the midpoint of AB.

1. $\frac{-8+6}{2} = \text{——} = ...$
2. $\frac{2+10}{2} = \text{——} = ...$
3. Coordinates of midpoint: (......, ...)

Straight-Line Equations

'x = a' is a line through 'a' on the (e.g. x = –3)

'y = a' is a line through 'a' on the (e.g. y = –1)

The x-axis is $y =$ .....
and the y-axis is $x =$ .....

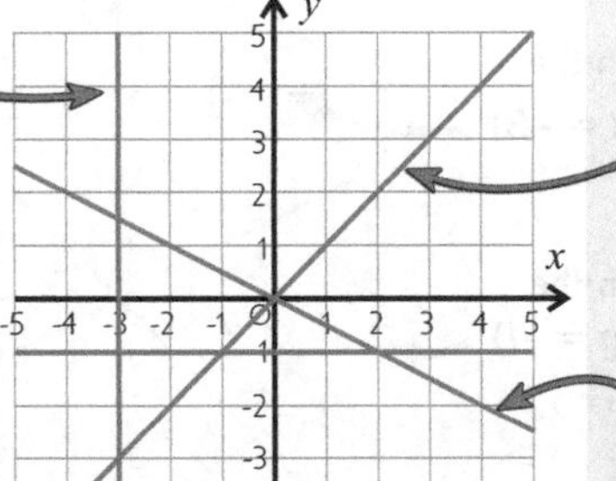

'y = x' is the through the

'y = ax' is a diagonal through the with 'a' (e.g. $y = -\frac{1}{2}x$)

Second Go:
...../...../.....

Coordinates and Straight Lines

Coordinates and Quadrants

Coordinates are written as:

is the

is the

To read coordinates,

The x- and y-coordinates can be

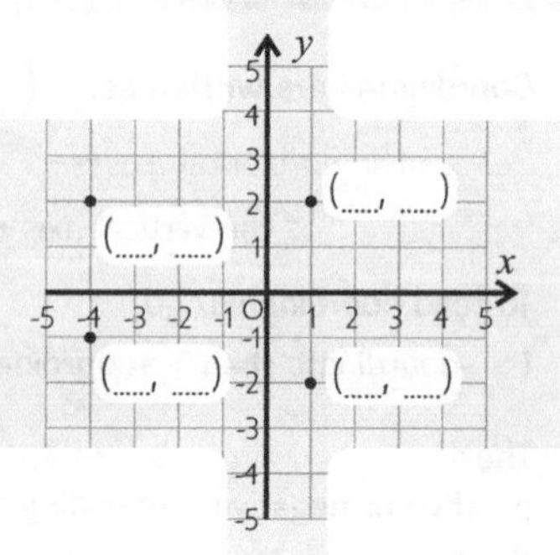

Midpoint of a Line

MIDPOINT OF A LINE SEGMENT —

Three steps to find the midpoint:

1. Find the
2. Find the
3. Put

EXAMPLE

Point A has coordinates (–8, 2) and Point B has coordinates (6, 10). Find the coordinates of the midpoint of AB.

① ——— = —— = ... ② ——— = —— = ...

③ Coordinates of midpoint: ....

Straight-Line Equations

'x = a' is a through 'a' on the (e.g. x = –3)

'y = a' is a through 'a' on the (e.g. y = –1)

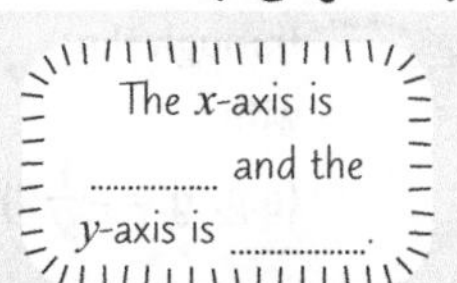

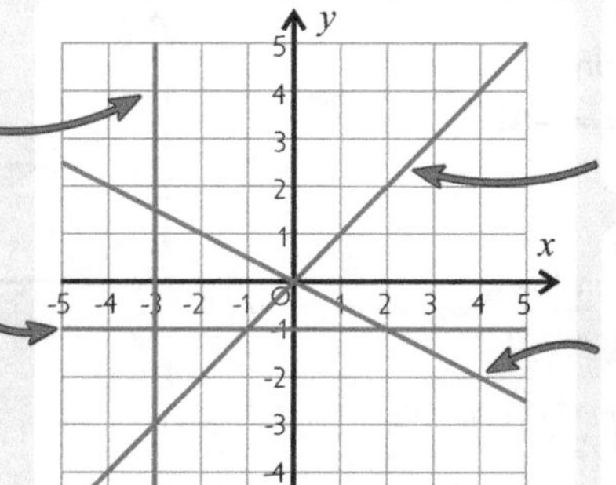

'y = x' is the

'y = ax' is a

with gradient (e.g. $y = -\frac{1}{2}x$)

Drawing Straight-Line Graphs

First Go: ..... /..... /.....

Spotting Straight-Line Equations

Straight-line equations only have an , a and a term.

If there are any other terms, .

....:

$y = 5x - 2$ $x + 2y = 1$

$3 + 4x - 2y = 0$ $8y = 1$

....:

$y = 3x^2 + 1$ $xy = 1$

$x^2 + y^2 = 3$ $5 = 3y - \frac{2}{x}$

Three Steps for Drawing

1. Draw a table with three .
2. Put the into the equation and work out the .
3. the points and draw a through them.

EXAMPLE

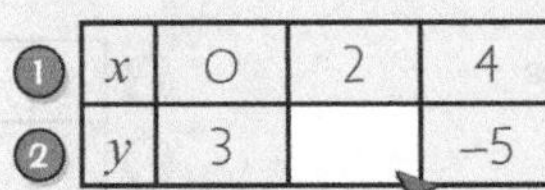

Draw the graph $y = -2x + 3$ for values of x from 0 to 4.

① x	0	2	4
② y	3		−5

E.g. when $x = 2$,

$y = -2(\ \ ) + 3$

$= \ \ + 3 =$

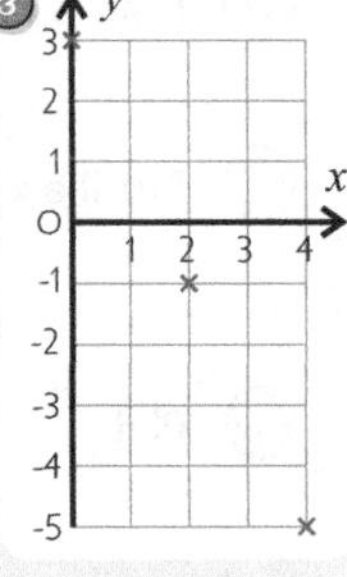

Finding the Gradient

GRADIENT — of a line.

Uphill slope = ... gradient

Downhill slope = ... gradient

Gradient = $\frac{\text{change in}}{\text{change in}}$

Three steps to find the gradient:

1. Find the of two points on the line.
2. Find the in y and the in x.
3. Substitute into the .

EXAMPLE

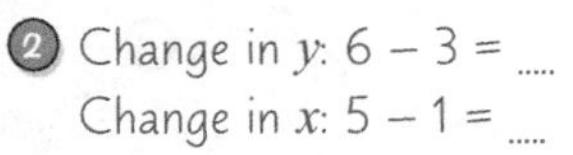

① A: (1, 3) B: (5, 6)

② Change in y: 6 − 3 = ...

Change in x: 5 − 1 = ...

③ Gradient = $\frac{.....}{.....}$ = ...

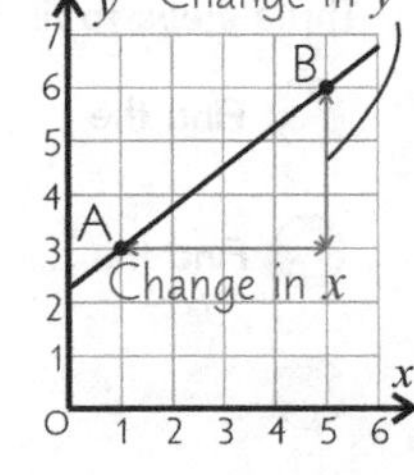

Subtract the y- and x-coordinates in ....

Second Go: ..... /..... /.....

Drawing Straight-Line Graphs

Spotting Straight-Line Equations

Straight-line equations only have

If there are

Straight lines:

Give some examples.

NOT straight lines:

Three Steps for Drawing

1. Draw a table
2. Put the x-values
3. Plot

EXAMPLE

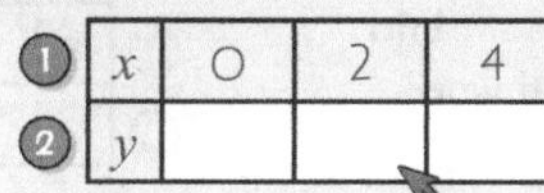

Draw the graph $y = -2x + 3$ for values of x from 0 to 4.

x	0	2	4
y			

E.g. when $x = 2$,

$y =$

$=$ $=$

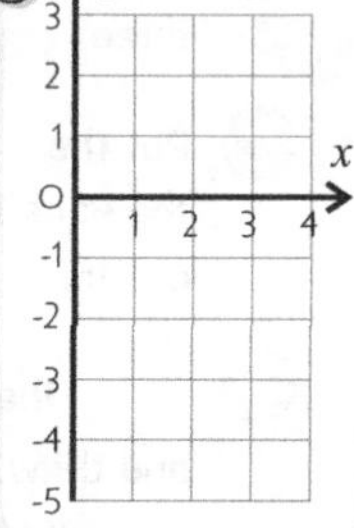

Finding the Gradient

GRADIENT — .

.... = ... gradient

.... = ... gradient

Gradient =

Three steps to find the gradient:

1. Find the
2. Find the
3.

EXAMPLE

1. A: .... B: ....
2. Change in y: ....
   Change in x: ....
3. Gradient = — = ...

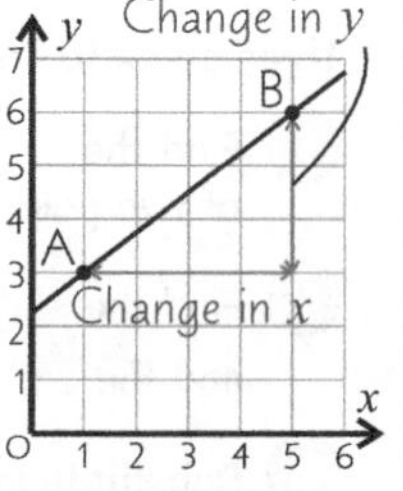

Subtract the .... in ....

y = mx + c

First Go: ..... /..... /.....

Equation of a Straight Line

General equation for a straight-line graph:

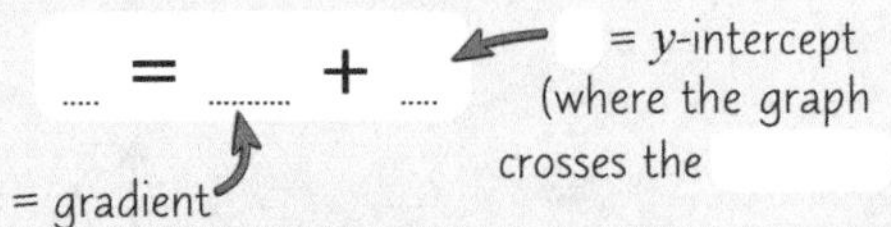

Rearrange other straight-line equations into this form:

$3x - y = 5$ ➡ $y =$ $-$

$7x + y - 2 = 0$ ➡ $y =$ $+$

Parallel lines have the ,
so they have the same :

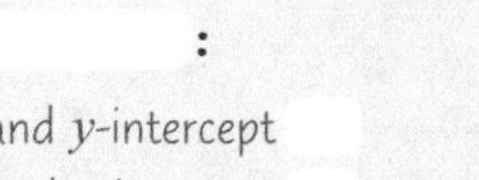

$y = 3x + 2$ has gradient and y-intercept

$y = 3x - 4$ has gradient and y-intercept

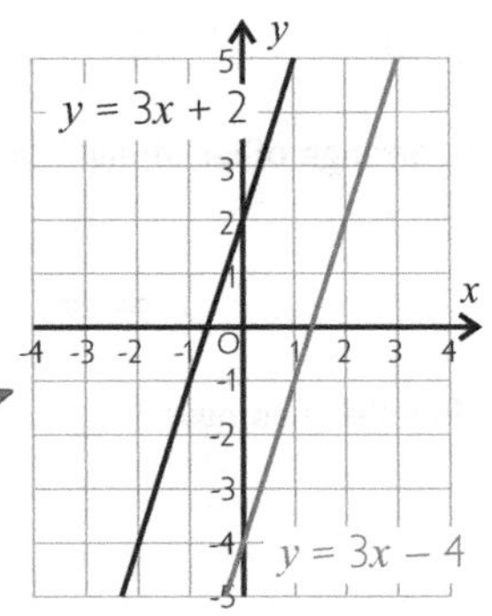

Three Steps to Find the Equation

1. **Use any** on the line to find the , 'm'.
2. **Read off the** , 'c'.
3. **Write equation as** .

EXAMPLE

Find the equation of this line in the form $y = mx + c$.

1. $m = \frac{6}{4} = \text{—}$
2. $c =$
3. $y =$ $x +$

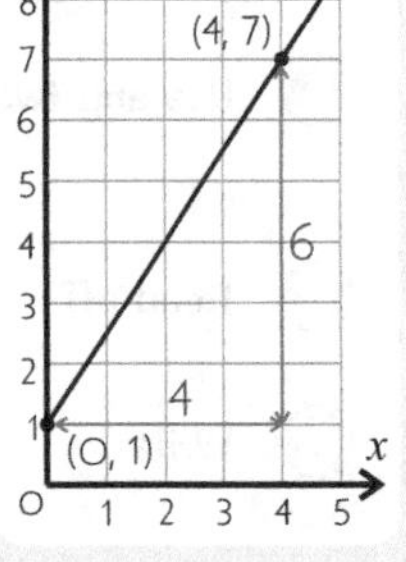

Equation of a Line Through Two Points

1. **Use both points to find** .
2. **Substitute one point into** .
3. **to find 'c'.**
4. **Write equation as** .

EXAMPLE

Find the equation of the straight line that passes through (–2, 12) and (4, –6).

1. $m = \frac{-6 - 12}{4 - (-2)} = \text{———} =$
2. Sub in (4, –6): $= -3(\quad) + c$
   $\Rightarrow \quad = \quad + c$
3. $c = \quad =$
4. $y =$

Second Go:
..... /..... /.....

y = mx + c

Equation of a Straight Line

General equation for a straight-line graph:

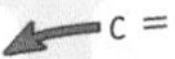

m =

Rearrange other straight-line equations into this form:

$3x - y = 5$ →

$7x + y - 2 = 0$ →

Parallel lines have

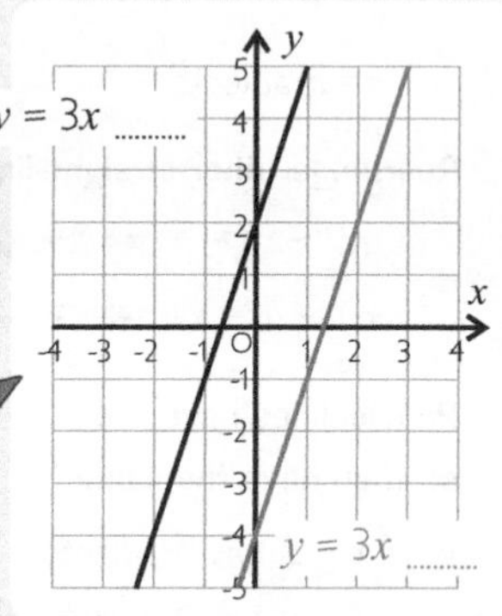

$y = 3x + 2$ has and

$y = 3x - 4$ has and

Three Steps to Find the Equation

1. **Use any two points**
2. **Read off**
3. **Write**

EXAMPLE

Find the equation of this line in the form $y = mx + c$.

1. m = —— = ——
2.
3.

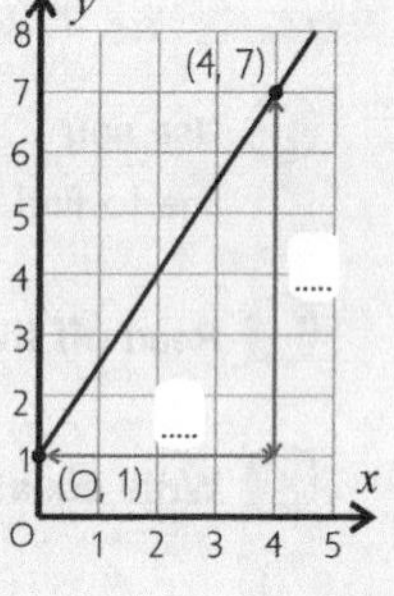

Equation of a Line Through Two Points

1. **Use**
2. **Substitute**
3. **Rearrange**
4. **Write**

EXAMPLE

Find the equation of the straight line that passes through (–2, 12) and (4, –6).

1. m = ———— = ——— =
2. Sub in (4, –6):
   ⇒
3. c =
4.

Quadratic Graphs

First Go: ...../...../.....

Quadratic Graphs

A quadratic graph (y =

but no higher powers)

has a symmetrical shape.

Three steps to plot a quadratic graph:

1. Substitute the into the equation to find .
2. the points.
3. Join the points with a .

If the coefficient of x^2 were negative, the curve would be ....

EXAMPLE

Plot the graph of $y = x^2 + 2x - 1$.

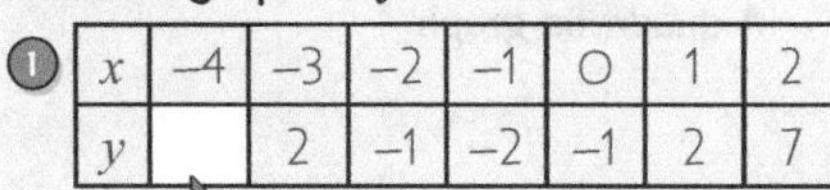

①

x	–4	–3	–2	–1	0	1	2
y		2	–1	–2	–1	2	7

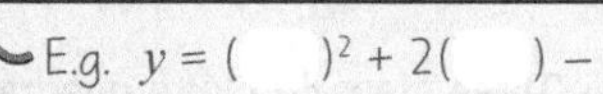

E.g. $y = (\quad)^2 + 2(\quad) - 1$

$= \quad - \quad - \quad =$

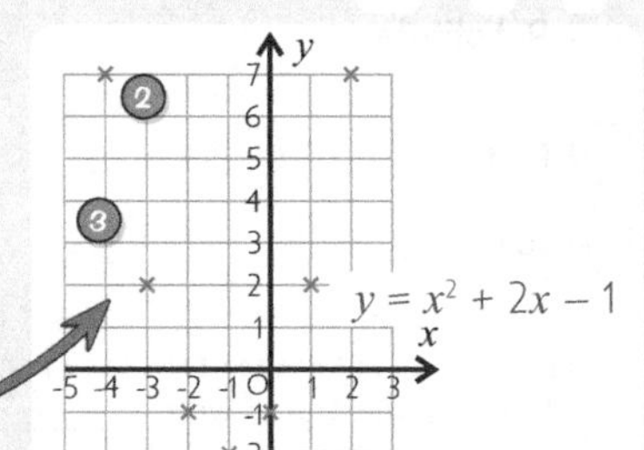

Three Steps to Find the Turning Point

1. Pick on the curve with the same .
2. Find the number between the .
   This is the x-coordinate of the turning point.
3. Put x to find y.

EXAMPLE

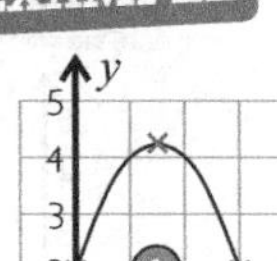

Find the turning point of $y = -x^2 + 3x + 2$.

② .... between $x = 0$ and $x = 3$ is ....

③ $y = -(\_\_\_\_)^2 + 3(\_\_\_\_) + 2$

$= -$ .... + ... + 2

= ....

Turning point: (........, ...)

Solving Quadratic Equations

ROOTS — x-values where a curve .

These are solutions to 'equation' = .

To find roots from a graph, read off the values where .

EXAMPLE

Use the graph to solve $2x^2 + 4x = 0$.

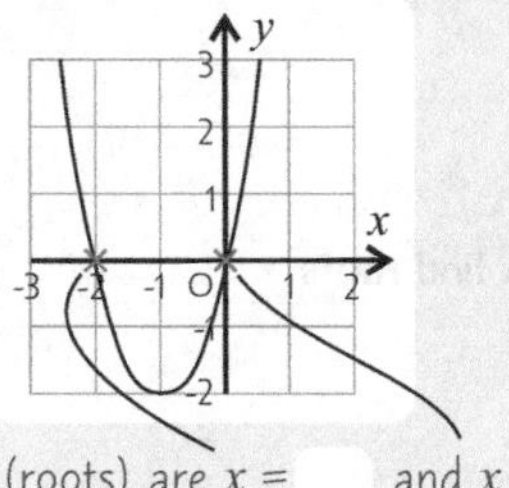

Solutions (roots) are $x =$ and $x =$.

Second Go:
...../...../.....

Quadratic Graphs

Quadratic Graphs

A quadratic graph

Three steps to plot a quadratic graph:

1. Substitute
2. Plot
3. Join

If the coefficient of x^2 were ....,
....

EXAMPLE

Plot the graph of $y = x^2 + 2x - 1$.

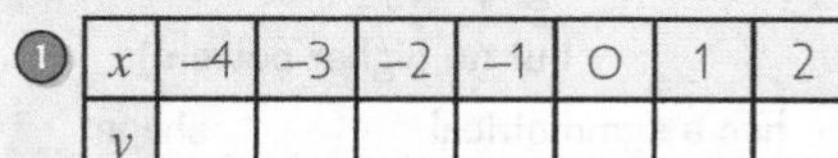

x	–4	–3	–2	–1	0	1	2
y							

E.g. $y =$

$=$ $=$

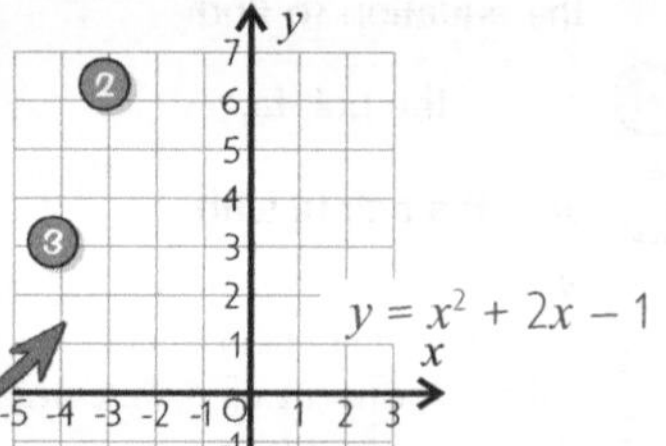

Three Steps to Find the Turning Point

1. Pick
2. Find

This is the x-coordinate of the turning point.

3. Put

EXAMPLE

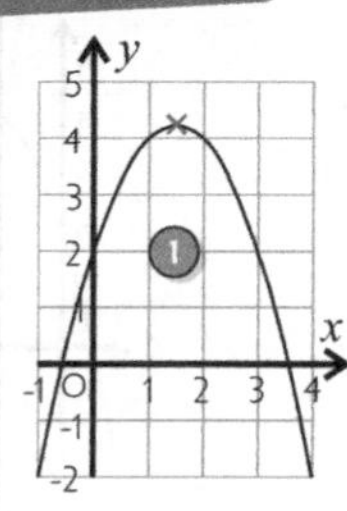

Find the turning point of $y = -x^2 + 3x + 2$.

2. Halfway between .... and .... is ....

3. $y =$ ....
$=$ ....
$=$ ....

Turning point:

Solving Quadratic Equations

ROOTS —

To find roots

EXAMPLE

Use the graph to solve $2x^2 + 4x = 0$.

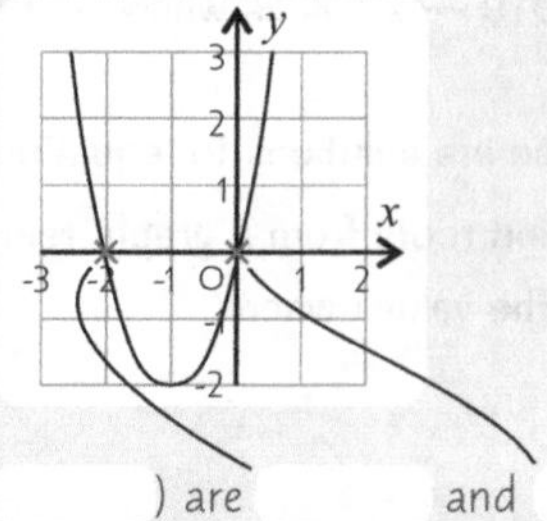

Solutions ( ) are and

Harder Graphs

First Go: ..... /..... /.....

Cubic Graphs

A cubic graph ($y =$, but no higher powers) has a in the middle.

$+x^3$ graphs go up from :

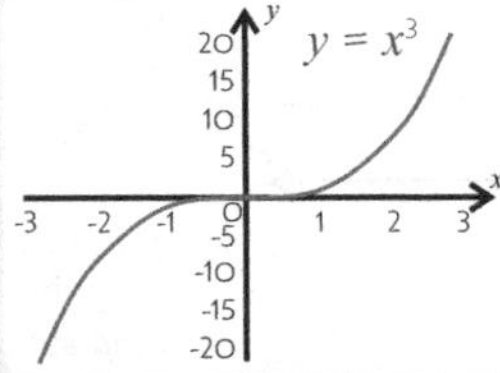

$-x^3$ graphs go down from :

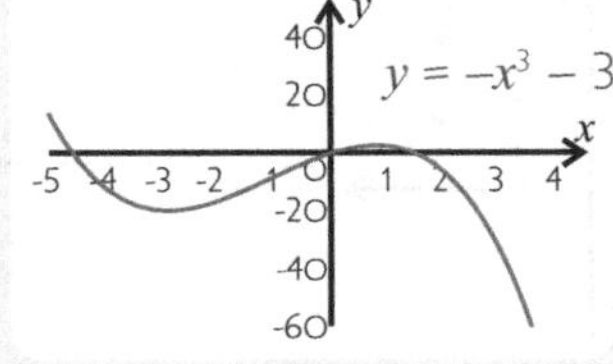

Plot cubic graphs using the steps for quadratic graphs.

Reciprocal Graphs

Equation: $y = \frac{\dots}{\dots}$

- Graphs have two symmetrical curves — one in the and one in the quadrant.
- Two halves of graph
- Curves never touch the
- about lines $y = x$ and $y = -x$.

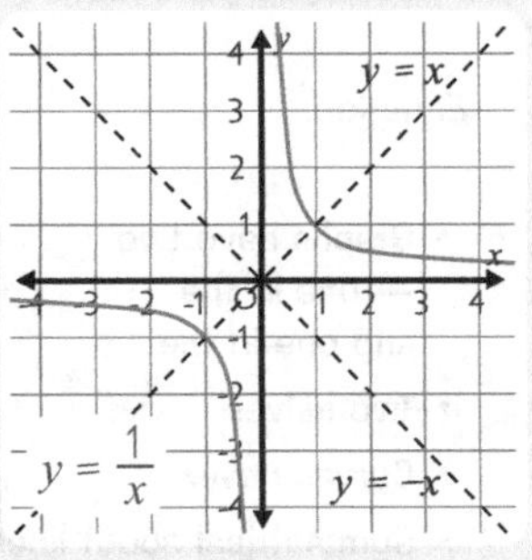

Solving Simultaneous Equations

1. Plot on a graph.
2. Read off the where the two lines .

To find the to an equation (e.g. $-2x = x - 3$), split it into two ($y = -2x$ and $y = x - 3$). Then follow the steps above.

EXAMPLE

By plotting the graphs, solve the simultaneous equations $y = -2x$ and $y = x - 3$.

1. 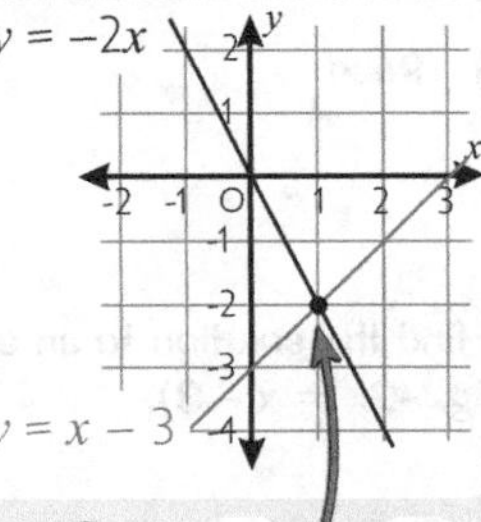

2. $x =$, $y =$

Second Go:
..... /..... /.....

Harder Graphs

Cubic Graphs

A cubic graph

$+x^3$ graphs go

:

$-x^3$ graphs go

:

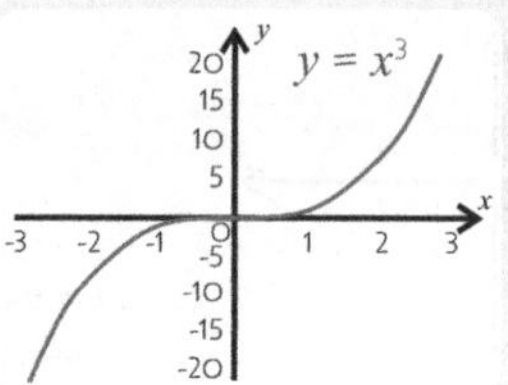

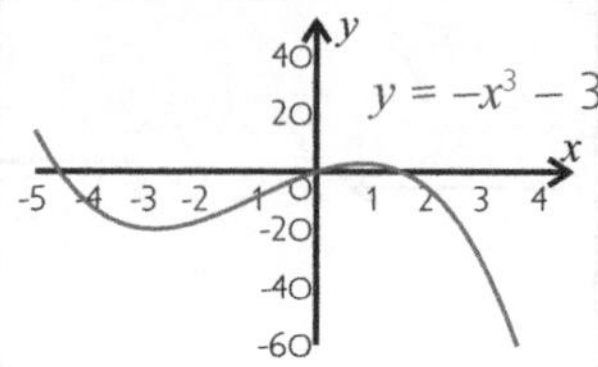

Plot cubic graphs using the steps for quadratic graphs.

Reciprocal Graphs

Equation:

- Graphs have two — one in the and one in the
- Two halves
- Curves never
- Symmetrical about lines

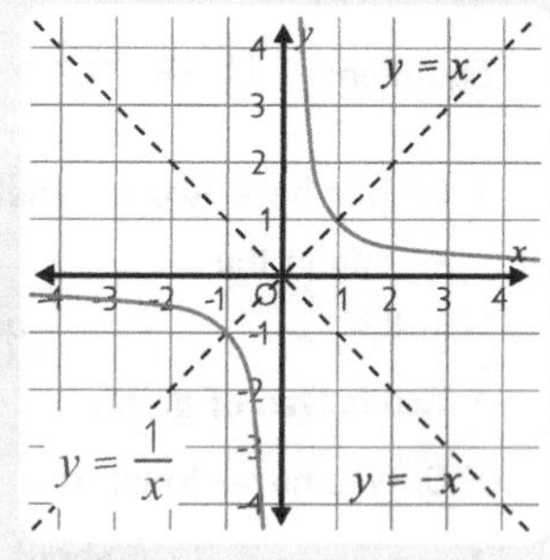

Solving Simultaneous Equations

Plot

Read

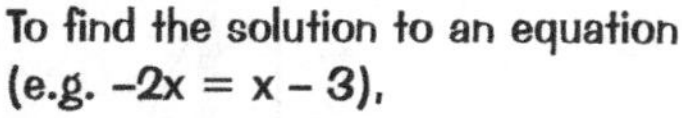
To find the solution to an equation (e.g. $-2x = x - 3$),

Then follow the steps above.

EXAMPLE

By plotting the graphs, solve the simultaneous equations $y = -2x$ and $y = x - 3$.

1

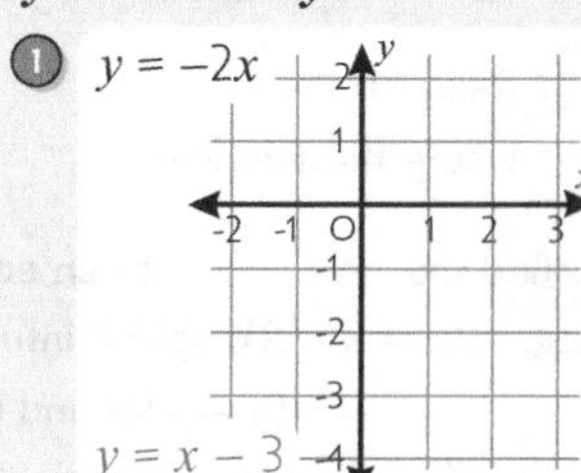

2

Distance-Time and Conversion Graphs

First Go: ..... /..... /.....

Distance-Time Graphs

DISTANCE-TIME GRAPHS — show ______________ against time.

Distance from the starting point goes on the ______________ and time goes on the ______________. The gradient gives the ______________.

EXAMPLE

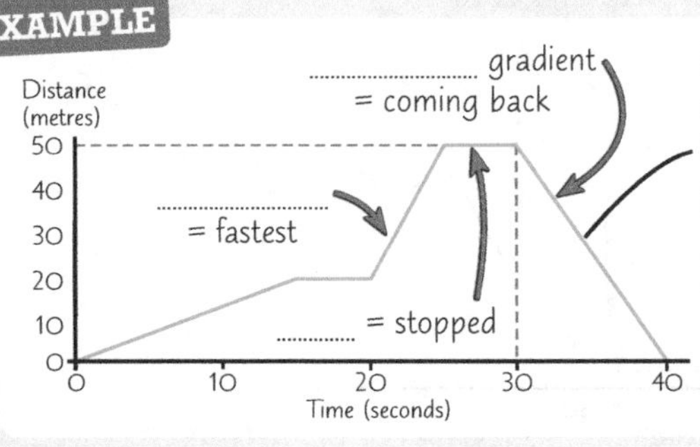

Final section starts 50 m from starting point at .... s and ends back at starting point at .... s.

Speed of this section

$= \frac{0-50}{40-30} = \frac{\dots\dots}{\dots\dots} = \dots\dots$ m/s,

so coming back at .... m/s.

Conversion Graphs

CONVERSION GRAPHS — show how to convert between ______________.

Three steps to use conversion graphs:

1. **Draw a line from a ______________.**
2. **When you reach the ______________, go to the other axis.**
3. **Read off the ______________ from this ______________.**

EXAMPLE

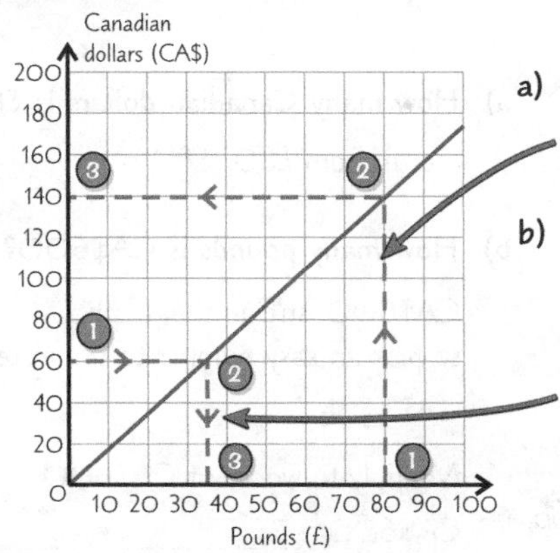

a) How many Canadian dollars is £80?

Go up from £80: £80 = CA$..........

b) How many pounds is CA$600?

CA$600 isn't on the graph, so pick an easy number to use instead:

CA$60 = £..........

Multiply to work out CA$600:

CA$600 = £........ × 10 = £..........

Second Go: ...../...../.....

Distance-Time and Conversion Graphs

Distance-Time Graphs

DISTANCE-TIME GRAPHS —

Distance from the

The gradient

EXAMPLE

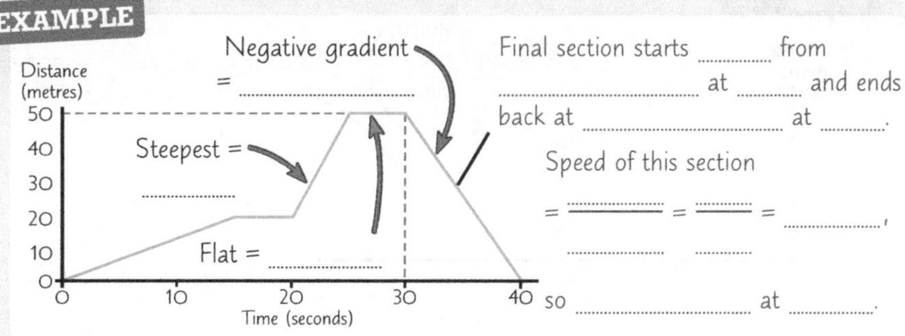

Final section starts .... from .... at .... and ends back at .... at ....

Speed of this section = $\frac{\text{..........}}{\text{..........}}$ = $\frac{\text{..........}}{\text{..........}}$ = ...,

so .... at ....

Conversion Graphs

CONVERSION GRAPHS — .

Three steps to use conversion graphs:

1. **Draw**
2. **When you reach**
3.  **Read**

EXAMPLE

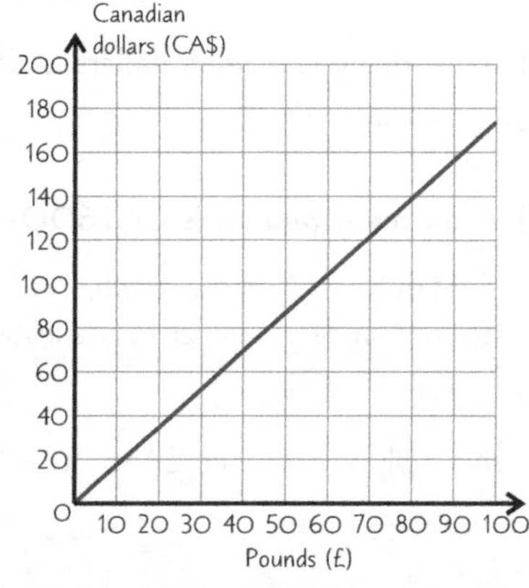

a) **How many Canadian dollars is £80?**

Go up from £80: £80 = ...

b) **How many pounds is CA$600?**

CA$600 isn't on the graph, so pick an easy number to use instead:

CA$........ = £........

Multiply to work out CA$600:

CA$600 = ... = ...

Real-Life Graphs and Rate of Change

First Go: ..... /..... /.....

Money Graphs

EXAMPLE

This graph shows the amount a company charges to ship an order.

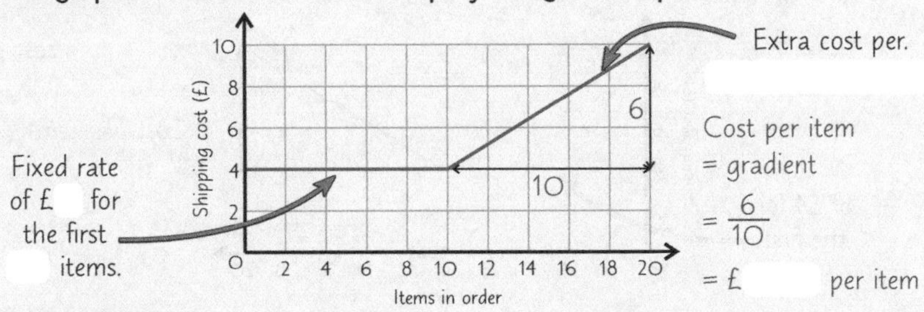

Rate of Change

RATE OF CHANGE — how something is changing.

- **Rate of change = .**
- **Steeper gradient = rate of change.**
- **Units: unit PER unit.**

To find the rate of change, work out the of the line, then add the .

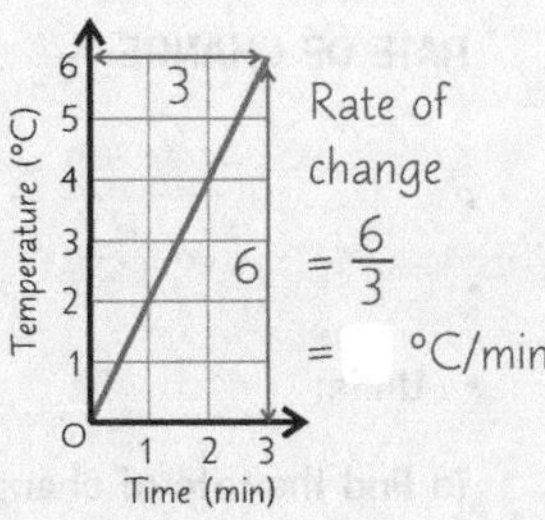

Changes with Time

EXAMPLE

Three jars are filled with sand at a constant rate.
These graphs show the height of sand in each jar.

Height rises faster when the jar is :

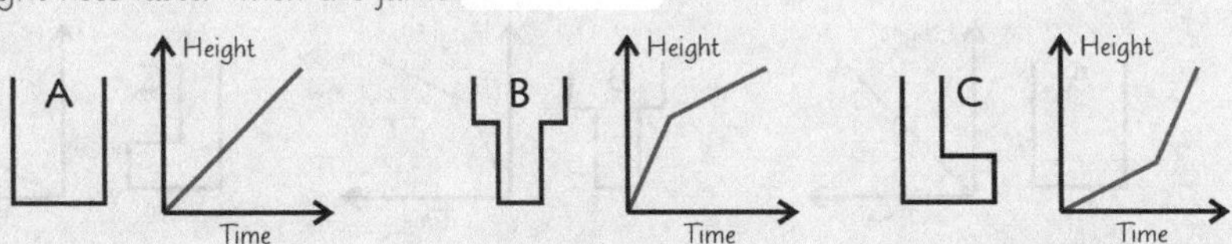

The jar has a , so the height rises at a .

The jar is narrow then wide, so the height rises then .

The jar is wide then narrow, so the height rises then .

Second Go: ..... /..... /.....

Real-Life Graphs and Rate of Change

Money Graphs

EXAMPLE

This graph shows the amount a company charges to ship an order.

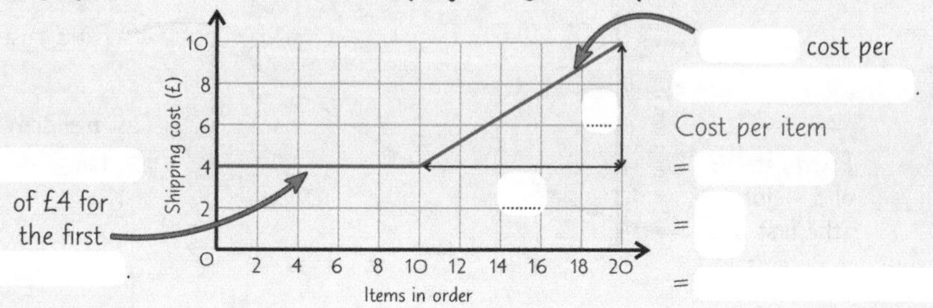

Rate of Change

RATE OF CHANGE —

- =
- = **rate of change.**
- **Units:**

To find the rate of change,

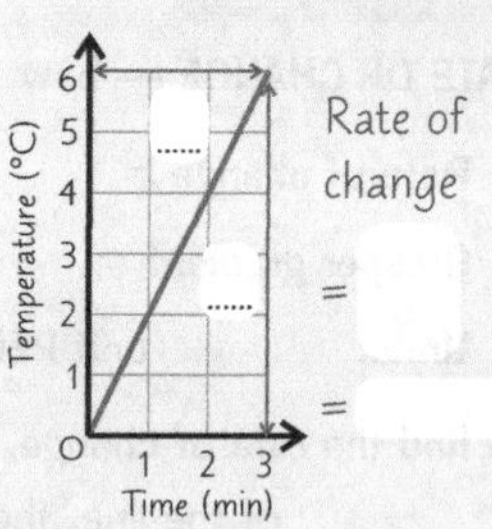

Changes with Time

EXAMPLE

Three jars are filled with sand at a constant rate.
These graphs show the height of sand in each jar.

Height rises faster when :

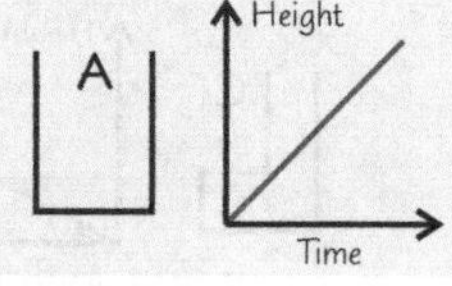

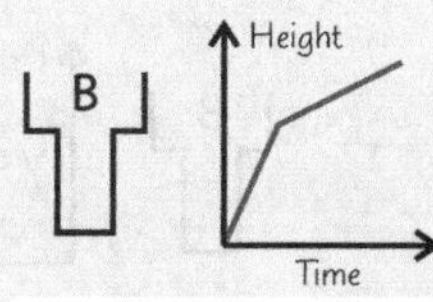

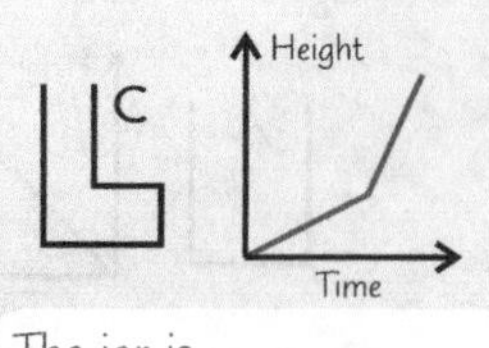

The jar has

The jar is

The jar is

Mixed Practice Quizzes

If a picture is worth a thousand words, how many is a graph worth? At least as many as are in these quizzes covering p.49-62, that much I know for certain.

Quiz 1

Date: ...... / ...... / ......

1) What does the graph of $y = x^3$ look like?
2) What is the equation of the horizontal line that passes through (3, 4)?
3) When finding the equation of a line through two points, what is the next step after working out the gradient?
4) A wide glass and a narrow glass are filled with water at a constant rate. Which one has a steeper gradient on a graph of water height against time?
5) In which quadrant are x-coordinates negative and y-coordinates positive?
6) What does the gradient tell you about a line?
7) What is the general equation for a straight-line graph?
8) What does a negative gradient on a distance-time graph mean?
9) What are the roots of an equation?
10) How do you use a conversion graph?

Total:

Quiz 2

Date: ...... / ...... / ......

1) What does c represent in $y = mx + c$?
2) How do you read coordinates?
3) What is the first step in solving $5x = 3x - 4$ using a graph?
4) About which two lines are reciprocal graphs symmetrical?
5) If a line has a downhill slope, is the gradient positive or negative?
6) What does a distance-time graph look like while an object is stopped?
7) Is $xy + y = 4$ a straight-line equation?
8) If a quadratic curve is upside down, what do you know about the equation?
9) True or false? $y = 4x + 6$ and $y = 3x + 6$ are parallel lines.
10) What is meant by 'rate of change'?

Total:

Mixed Practice Quizzes

Quiz 3

Date: ...... / ...... / ......

1) A km-to-miles conversion graph has 0 to 50 km on one axis. How could you use this graph to convert 200 km into miles?
2) What is the equation of the line through the origin with gradient 5?
3) What kind of graph has a symmetrical bucket shape?
4) To work out the gradient of the line through (1, 2) and (3, 4), Tim works out 4 – 2 and 1 – 3. What is his mistake?
5) What is the equation of a reciprocal graph?
6) How do you find the rate of change from a graph?
7) Line A is parallel to $y = -2x - 8$. What is the gradient of line A?
8) What is the midpoint of a line segment?
9) What does the gradient of a distance-time graph give?
10) How do you find the roots of a quadratic equation from a graph?

Total:

Quiz 4

Date: ...... / ...... / ......

1) Is $x = 2$ a vertical, horizontal or diagonal line?
2) How do you solve a pair of simultaneous equations using a graph?
3) What goes on the vertical axis of a distance-time graph?
4) What is the equation of the line with gradient –2 and y-intercept 1?
5) What is the first step in plotting a quadratic graph?
6) What is the formula for the gradient of a line?
7) A booking fee is £3 for up to 8 people, then £1 per additional person. Describe the graph of the booking fee against the number of people.
8) How can you use three values of x to draw a straight-line graph?
9) If a cubic graph goes down from the top left, is the coefficient of x^3 positive or negative?
10) What does a shallower gradient tell you about the rate of change?

Total:

Ratios

First Go: ..... /..... /.....

Four Ways to Simplify Ratios

1. ______ all numbers by the same thing.

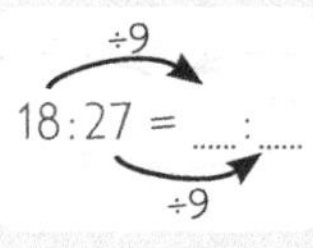

2. Multiply to get rid of ______ and ______.

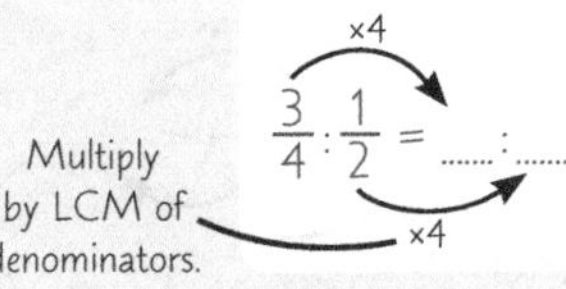

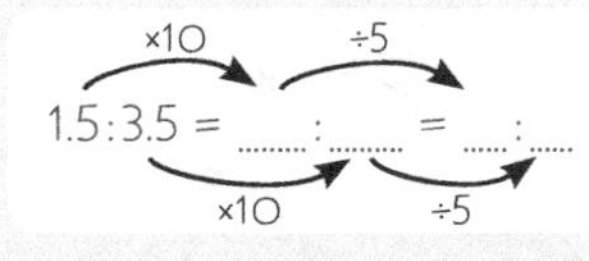

3. Convert to the ______.

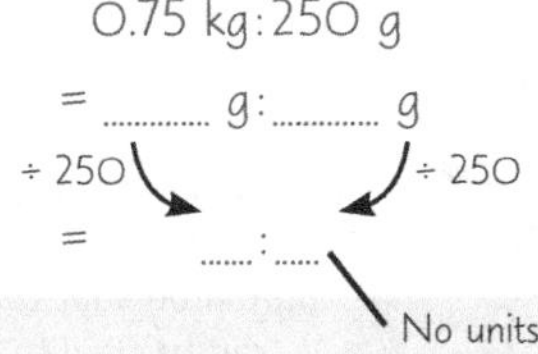

4. Divide to get in the form ______ or ______.

÷2
2:5 = ...:..... (or $1:\frac{5}{2}$)
÷2

The .... button on your calculator can be used to help simplify ratios.

Writing One Part as a Fraction of Another

Just write one number .... of the other.

EXAMPLE

Cats and dogs are in the ratio 3:2.

There are ______ as many cats as dogs, or there are ______ as many dogs as cats.

Two Steps to Write One Part as a Fraction of the Total

1. ______ to find the total number of parts.

2. Write the part you want over the ______.

EXAMPLE

In a car park, the ratio of cars to vans is 8:3.

1. There are ..... + ... = ... parts in total.

2. So $\frac{.....}{.....}$ are cars and $\frac{.....}{.....}$ are vans.

Second Go: ...../...../.....

Ratios

Four Ways to Simplify Ratios

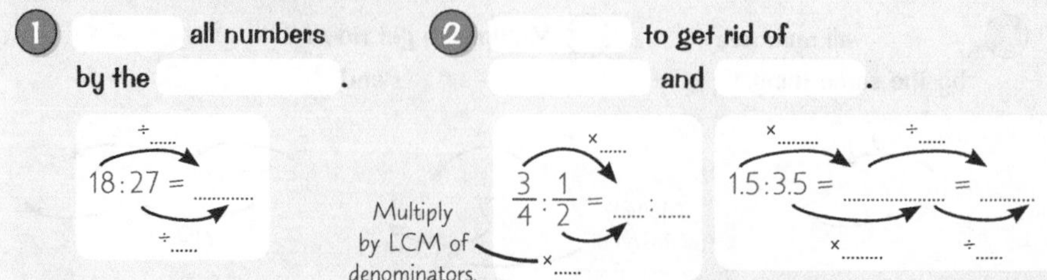

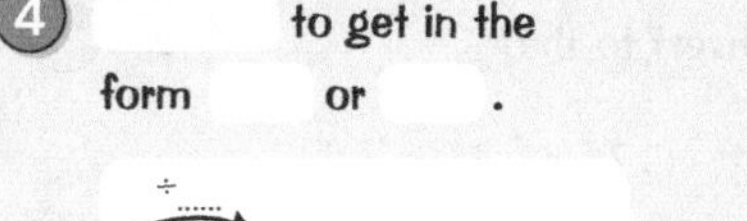

Multiply by LCM of denominators.

3 to the .
4 to get in the form or .

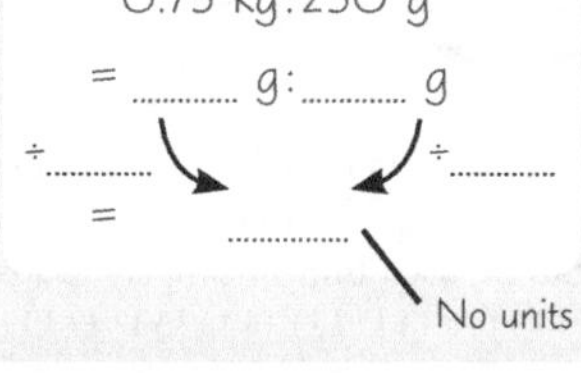

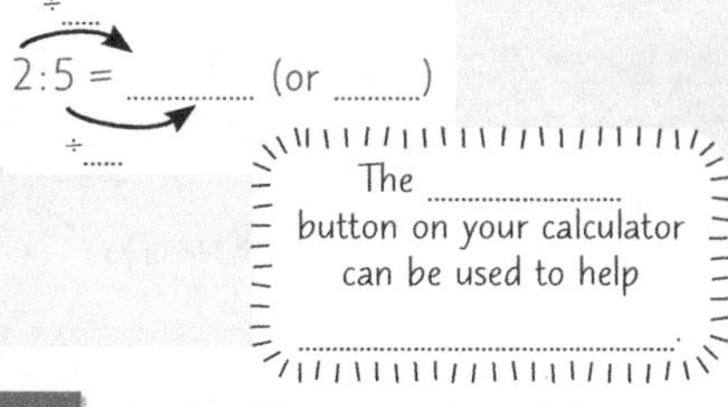

0.75 kg:250 g

Writing One Part as a Fraction of Another

Just write ....

EXAMPLE
1 There are .... in total.

Cats and dogs are in the ratio 3:2.

There are as many ,

or there are as many .

Two Steps to Write One Part as a Fraction of the Total

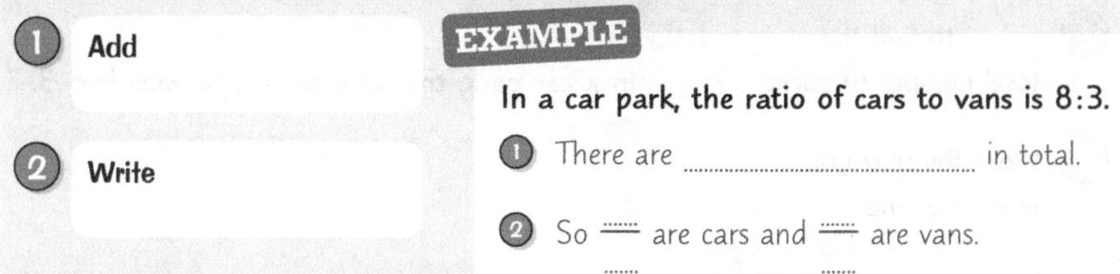

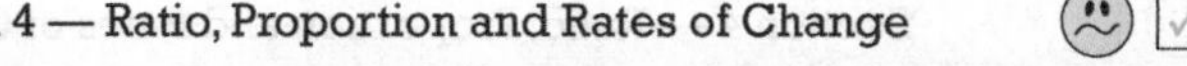

More Ratios

First Go: ...../...../.....

Three Steps to Scale Up Ratios

1. Work out what one side of the ratio is ______ to get its actual value.
2. Multiply the ______ ______ by this number.
3. ______ the two sides to find the ______ (if the question asks you to).

The two sides of a ratio are always in ....

EXAMPLE

A theatre audience is made up of adults and children in the ratio 3:5. There are 120 adults. How many people are there in the audience in total?

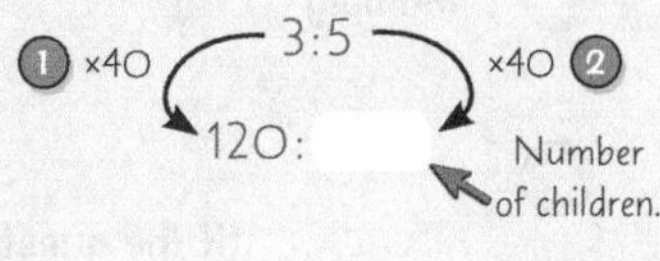

3 ______ + ______ = ______ people

Part : Whole Ratios

PART : WHOLE RATIO — ______ side of ratio included in ______ side.

part : part → part : whole

______ to find the whole.

part : whole → part : part

______ the part you know from the ______ to find the other part.

EXAMPLE

Fiction and non-fiction books are in the ratio 3:7.

Total parts = ... + ... = ...

Ratio of fiction to total books is ....:........

Ratio of non-fiction to total books is ....:.........

EXAMPLE

Kei has red and grey socks. The ratio of red socks to all of his socks is 5:8.

..... − ..... = ... parts are grey. So ratio of red socks to grey socks is .....:.....

Three Steps for Proportional Division

1. ______ the parts.
2. ______ to find one part.
3. ______ to find the amounts.

EXAMPLE

1200 g of flour is used to make cakes, pastry and bread in the ratio 8:7:9. How much flour is used to make pastry?

1. ______ + ______ + ______ = ______ parts
2. 1 part = ______ g ÷ ______ = ______ g
3. 7 parts = ______ × ______ g = ______ g

   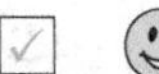 

Second Go:
...../...../.....

More Ratios

Three Steps to Scale Up Ratios

1. Work out what one side of the ratio is
2. Multiply
3. (if the question asks you to).

EXAMPLE

A theatre audience is made up of adults and children in the ratio 3:5. There are 120 adults. How many people are there in the audience in total?

1 × 3:5 × 2

Number of children.

3

The .... are always in ....

Part : Whole Ratios

PART : WHOLE RATIO — .

part : part → part : whole	part : whole → part : part
Add	Subtract

EXAMPLE

Fiction and non-fiction books are in the ratio 3:7.

Total parts = ...

Ratio of fiction to .... books is ....

Ratio of non-fiction to .... books is ....

EXAMPLE

Kei has red and grey socks. The ratio of red socks to all of his socks is 5:8.

.... parts are grey. So ratio of red socks to grey socks is ....

Three Steps for Proportional Division

1. Add up
2. Divide
3. Multiply

EXAMPLE

1200 g of flour is used to make cakes, pastry and bread in the ratio 8:7:9. How much flour is used to make pastry?

1

2 1 part =

3 7 parts =

Direct Proportion

First Go: ..... /..... /.....

Two Steps for Direct Proportion

DIRECT PROPORTION — two amounts or together, at the .

1. to find the amount for one thing.
2. to find the amount for the number of things you want.

EXAMPLE

3 footballs cost £29.70. How much do 7 footballs cost?

1. 1 football costs £ ÷ = £
2. 7 footballs cost £ × = £

Two Steps for Scaling Recipes

1. to find the amount for one person.
2. to find the amount for the number of people you want.

EXAMPLE

A smoothie recipe for 6 people uses 900 ml of apple juice. How much apple juice is needed to make smoothies for 4 people?

1. For 1 person you need ml ÷ = ml of apple juice
2. For 4 people you need ml × = ml of apple juice

Two Steps to Find the Best Buy

1. For each item, amount by price in pence to get amount per .
2. amounts per penny to find the .

You can also divide the price by the amount (length, mass, etc.) to get the .... A smaller cost per unit means ....

EXAMPLE

Some wrapping paper comes in rolls of two lengths, as shown.

Which roll is better value for money?

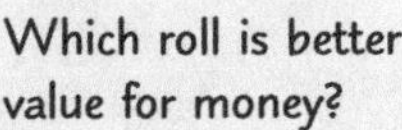

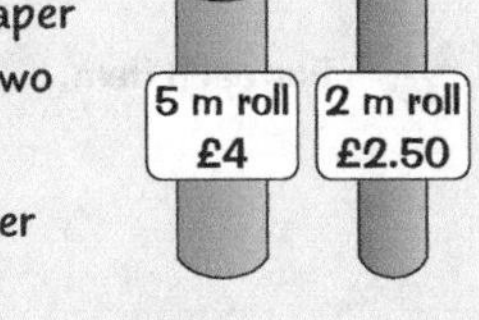

1. 5 m = cm — It's easier if you convert m to cm.
   £4 = p — Convert £ to p.
   cm ÷ p = cm per penny.
   2 m = cm
   £2.50 = p
   cm ÷ p = cm per penny.
2. The roll is better value as you get more paper per penny. — More per penny means better value for money.

Second Go:
..... /..... /.....

Direct Proportion

Two Steps for Direct Proportion

DIRECT PROPORTION —

1. **Divide**
2. **Multiply**

EXAMPLE

3 footballs cost £29.70.
How much do 7 footballs cost?

1. 1 football costs
2. 7 footballs cost

Two Steps for Scaling Recipes

1. **Divide**
2. **Multiply**

EXAMPLE

A smoothie recipe for 6 people uses 900 ml of apple juice. How much apple juice is needed to make smoothies for 4 people?

1. For 1 person you need
2. For 4 people you need

Two Steps to Find the Best Buy

1. **For each item,**
2. **Compare**

You can also .... the price by the .... (................, ..., etc.) to get the .... A smaller cost per unit means ....

EXAMPLE

Some wrapping paper comes in rolls of two lengths, as shown.
Which roll is better value for money?

5 m roll £4 | 2 m roll £2.50

1. 5 m =
   £4 =
   =
   2 m =
   £2.50 =
   =
2.

It's easier if you convert m to cm.
Convert £ to p.

Direct and Inverse Proportion

First Go:
...../...../.....

Graphing Direct Proportion

Two things in direct proportion make a graph.

- Line goes through the .
- All direct proportions can be written as an of the form:

y = A is a number.

- To find A, given values into the equation.

EXAMPLE

The amount of paint needed to paint a wall is directly proportional to its area. 12 litres of paint are needed for an area of 100 m².

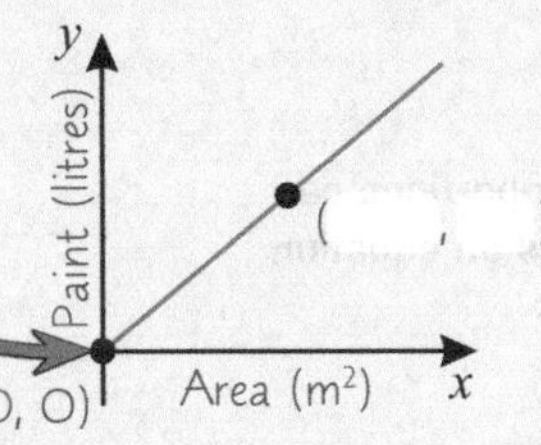

$12 = A \times 100$, so A = ÷ =

So $y =$

Two Steps for Inverse Proportion

INVERSE PROPORTION — one amount as the other , at the . E.g. when one amount doubles, the other .

1. to find the amount for one thing.
2. to find the amount for the number of things you want.

EXAMPLE

It takes two people 5 minutes to peel 30 potatoes. How long would it take five people to peel 30 potatoes at the same rate?

1. 30 potatoes would take one person × = minutes
2. Five people would take ÷ = minutes

Graphing Inverse Proportion

Two things in inverse proportion make a graph that from .

- Curve doesn't go through the .
- All inverse proportions can be written as an of the form:

y = — A is a number.

- To find A, given values into the equation.

EXAMPLE

y is inversely proportional to x. When $x = 2$, $y = 4$.

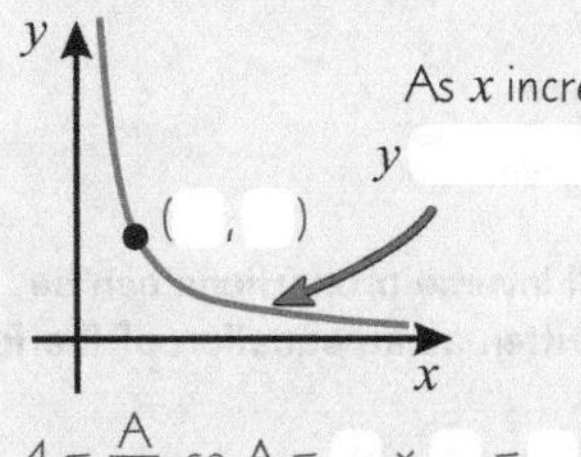

$4 = \frac{A}{2}$, so A = × =

So $y =$

Second Go:
..... /..... /.....

Direct and Inverse Proportion

Graphing Direct Proportion

Two things in

- Line
- All direct proportions can be written as an equation of the form:
- To find A,

EXAMPLE

The amount of paint needed to paint a wall is directly proportional to its area. 12 litres of paint are needed for an area of 100 m^2.

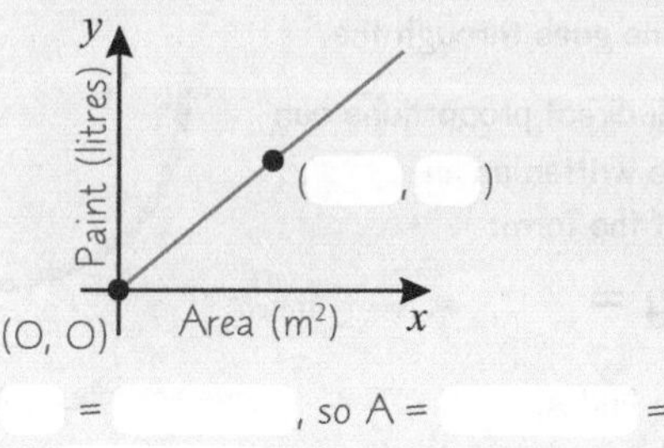

= , so A = =

So

Two Steps for Inverse Proportion

INVERSE PROPORTION —

E.g. when

1. Multiply
2. Divide

EXAMPLE

It takes two people 5 minutes to peel 30 potatoes. How long would it take five people to peel 30 potatoes at the same rate?

1. 30 potatoes would take one person
2. Five people would take

Graphing Inverse Proportion

Two things in

- Curve
- All inverse proportions can be written as an equation of the form:
- To find A,

EXAMPLE

y is inversely proportional to x. When $x = 2$, $y = 4$.

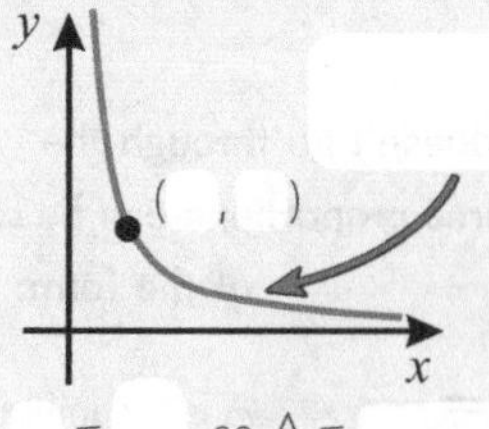

= , so A = =

So

Mixed Practice Quizzes

Have a go at these quizzes, all about what you've learned on p.65-72, then mark your answers. It's a very generous ratio of questions to pages, if you ask me...

Quiz 1

Date: ...... / ...... / ......

1) Simplify: a) 5:15 b) 21:12
2) True or false? If 2:7 is a part:whole ratio, 2:5 is the part:part ratio.
3) What does a direct proportion graph look like?
4) What is the first step to simplify the ratio 300 g : 1.5 kg?
5) On a school trip, there are $\frac{11}{2}$ as many students as teachers. What is the ratio of students to teachers?
6) What are the two steps needed to solve direct proportion problems?
7) True or false? An inverse proportion graph always goes through the origin.
8) 240 g of flour makes 8 scones. How much flour is needed for 1 scone?
9) In Jar A you get 4.6 g of jam per penny. In Jar B you get 5 g of jam per penny. Which jar of jam is better value for money?
10) What is the general equation of an inverse proportion curve?

Total:

Quiz 2

Date: ...... / ...... / ......

1) £150 is shared in the ratio 2:3:5. What is the value of one part?
2) What are the two steps needed to solve inverse proportion problems?
3) How do you simplify a ratio that contains decimals?
4) A bunch of flowers contains only red and white flowers in the ratio 3:5. What is the ratio of the red flowers to all of the flowers?
5) A is inversely proportional to B. If A doubles in size, what happens to B?
6) 5 stickers cost £3. What is the first step to find the cost of 12 stickers?
7) How do you write one part of a ratio as a fraction of another part?
8) 600 ml of juice costs £1.20. How much juice do you get per penny?
9) If $y = \frac{A}{x}$ and $y = 8$ when $x = 2$, find the value of A.
10) What is the next thing you'd do to scale up a ratio, after working out what one side of the ratio is multiplied by?

Total:

Mixed Practice Quizzes

Quiz 3

Date: ...... / ...... / ......

1) How do you write a ratio in the form 1:n?
2) A box of chocolates contains only white and milk chocolates in the ratio 3:7. What fraction of the box is white chocolates?
3) What is the first thing you would do to share 200 g in the ratio 3:2?
4) y is directly proportional to x, and when x = 2, y = 5. Give two points that the graph of this proportion would go through.
5) True or false? The two sides of a ratio are always in inverse proportion.
6) How do you find the other part of a ratio from a part:whole ratio?
7) If y = Ax and y = 20 when x = 4, find the value of A.
8) What does an inverse proportion graph look like?
9) How do you write one part of a ratio as a fraction of the total?
10) A sum of money is shared in the ratio 5:3. If 1 part = £10, what is the value of the larger share?

Total:

Quiz 4

Date: ...... / ...... / ......

1) What would be the first step in simplifying a ratio that contains fractions?
2) If two amounts are in direct proportion and one amount doubles, what happens to the other amount?
3) Salad dressing is made from vinegar and oil in the ratio 2:5. How much vinegar is needed to make salad dressing with 500 ml of oil?
4) What is the general equation of a direct proportion graph?
5) A field contains sheep and cows. The ratio of sheep to all animals in the field is 4:7. What is the ratio of sheep to cows?
6) Give the ratio 2:3 in the form 1:n.
7) What is the next step in proportional division, after adding up the parts?
8) A recipe serves 6 people. How would you scale it up to serve 10 people?
9) A pot contains pens and pencils in the ratio 2:7. There are 4 pens. How many pencils are there?
10) What is the first step to work out which item is the best value for money?

Total:

Percentages

First Go: ..... /..... /.....

Finding Percentages of Amounts

'Per cent' means 'out of '.

E.g. 30% means '30 out of ' = =

To find 10%, divide by .... To find 5%, find .... then divide by .... To find 1%, divide by ....

Two steps for '% of' questions:

1. Change percentage to a .
2. Replace 'of' with and .

EXAMPLE

Find 45% of 80.

1. 45% = ...
2. 0.45 × 80 = ...

x as a Percentage of y

1. Divide by .
2. Multiply by .

EXAMPLE

Write 30 as a percentage of 250.

1. $\frac{30}{250}$ = — Simplify fraction first if you don't have a calculator.
2. × = %

Two Methods for Percentage Change

Find Percentage then or :

1. Find of original amount.
2. to/ from original value.

EXAMPLE

Increase £25 by 20%.

1. 20% of £25
 = × £25
 = £ — It's an increase, so add.
2. £ + £ = £

The Multiplier Method:

MULTIPLIER — you multiply original value by to it by a %.

% increase — multiplier is

% decrease — multiplier is

Two steps for using multipliers:

1. Find multiplier — write % change as a and add to/subtract from .
2. Multiply by multiplier.

EXAMPLE

A scarf originally cost £7.50. Its price is reduced by 12%. Find the new price.

1. 12% =
 Multiplier for 12% decrease
 = − =
2. New price of scarf
 = £ × = £

Second Go:
..... /..... /.....

Percentages

Finding Percentages of Amounts

'Per cent' means ' '.

E.g. 30% means ' ' = =

To find 10%, ...
To find 5%, ...
.... To find 1%,
....

Two steps for '% of' questions:

1. Change
2. Replace

EXAMPLE

Find 45% of 80.

1. 45% =
2.

x as a Percentage of y

1. Divide
2. Multiply

EXAMPLE

Write 30 as a percentage of 250.

1. = — Simplify fraction first if you don't have a calculator.
2. = 12%

Two Methods for Percentage Change

Find Percentage then :

1. Find
2.

EXAMPLE

Increase £25 by 20%.

1. 20% of £25
   =
   =
2. =

The Multiplier Method:

MULTIPLIER —

% increase —

% decrease —

Two steps for using multipliers:

1. Find multiplier —
2. Multiply

EXAMPLE

A scarf originally cost £7.50.
Its price is reduced by 12%.
Find the new price.

1. =
   Multiplier for 12%
   = =
2. New price of scarf
   =
   =

More Percentages

First Go:
..... /..... /.....

Simple Interest

SIMPLE INTEREST — a % of the ______ is paid at regular intervals (e.g. every year). The amount of interest ______.

Three steps for simple interest questions:

1. Find the ______ earned each time.
2. ______ by the number of intervals.
3. ______ to original value (if needed).

EXAMPLE

Lila puts £2500 in a savings account that pays 2% simple interest each year. How much will be in the account after 5 years?

1. 2% of £2500
   = ______ × £2500 = £ ______
2. 5 × £ ______ = £ ______ — Total interest earned
3. £2500 + £ ______ = £ ______

Finding the Percentage Change

'______' = increase, decrease, profit, loss, etc.

Percentage change = $\frac{\quad}{\quad}$ × 100

Two steps to find the percentage change:

1. Find the change between the ______.
2. Put values into the ______.

EXAMPLE

A car was bought for £11 500. It is sold for £8855. Find the percentage loss.

1. Loss = £ ______ − £ ______
   = £ ______
2. % loss = $\frac{\quad}{\quad}$ × ______
   = ______ × ______
   = ______ %

Three Steps to Find the Original Value

1. Write the amount as a ______ of the ______.
2. Divide to find ______ of the original value.
3. Multiply by ______ to find the original value (100%).

EXAMPLE

A village has a population of 960. The population of the village has increased by 20% since 2016. What was the population in 2016?

1. 960 = ______ %
2. 960 ÷ ______ = ______ % ÷ ______
   ______ = 1%
3. ______ × ______ = 1% × ______
   ______ = 100%

So the population in 2016 was ______.

Second Go: ...../...../.....

More Percentages

Simple Interest

SIMPLE INTEREST —

Three steps for simple interest questions:

1. Find
2. Multiply
3. Add (if needed).

EXAMPLE

Lila puts £2500 in a savings account that pays 2% simple interest each year. How much will be in the account after 5 years?

1. 2% of £2500
   =
   =
2. Total interest earned
3.

Finding the Percentage Change

'Change' = , , , , etc.

Percentage change =

Two steps to find the percentage change:

1. Find
2. Put values

EXAMPLE

A car was bought for £11 500. It is sold for £8855. Find the percentage loss.

1. Loss =
   =
2. % loss =
   =
   =

Three Steps to Find the Original Value

1. Write
2. Divide
3. Multiply

EXAMPLE

A village has a population of 960. The population of the village has increased by 20% since 2016. What was the population in 2016?

1. 960 =
2. =
   =
3. =
   = 100%

So the population in 2016 was .

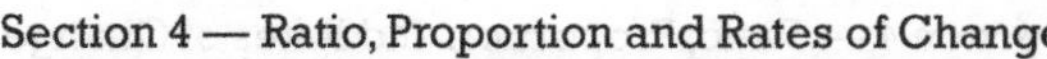

Compound Growth and Units

First Go: ..... /..... /.....

Compound Growth and Decay

COMPOUND GROWTH/DECAY — the amount added on/taken away (it's a % of the , rather than the original).

.... is an example of compound decay.

Formula for compound growth and decay:

Amount after n years/days/hours etc. → $N = N_0 \times (\text{multiplier})^n$ ← Number of years/days/hours etc.

EXAMPLE

Callum invests £4800 in a savings account that pays 2% compound interest each year. How much will there be in the account after 3 years?

N_0 = £4800, multiplier = ... + ... = ..., n = 3

Amount after 3 years = £................. × ....

= £.......................... (to the nearest penny)

You could also work this out by finding the amount .... E.g. after 1 year there's £4800 × .... = £4896, after 2 years there's £4896 × .... = £4993.92, etc.

Converting Units

Metric conversions:

1 cm = mm **1 tonne = kg**

1 = 100 cm **1 = 1000 ml**

1 km = m **1 litre = cm^3**

1 = 1000 g **1 cm^3 = ml**

Three steps for converting units:

1. **Find .**
2. **and by it.**
3. **Choose answer.**

Think which unit there should be ....

For metric-imperial conversions, conversion factors will be given.

EXAMPLE

Thandi runs 3500 m. How far does she run in km?

1. 1 km = ,
   so conversion factor =
2. 3500 × =
   3500 ÷ =
   Cross out incorrect working.
3. 3500 m = — Add units.

EXAMPLE

A tank holds 18 gallons of fuel. Given 1 gallon ≈ 4.5 litres, how much fuel can the tank hold in litres?

1. Conversion factor =
2. 18 × =
   18 ÷ =
   Cross out incorrect working.
3. 18 gallons ≈

Second Go:
...../...../.....

Compound Growth and Units

Compound Growth and Decay

COMPOUND GROWTH/DECAY —

Depreciation is ....

Formula for compound growth and decay:

Amount after n years/days/hours etc. →   ← Number of years/days/hours etc.

Initial amount   % change multiplier

EXAMPLE

Callum invests £4800 in a savings account that pays 2% compound interest each year. How much will there be in the account after 3 years?

N_0 = ..., multiplier = ..., n = ...

Amount after 3 years = ...

= .... (to the nearest penny)

You could also work this out by finding the amount each year. E.g. after 1 year there's .... = ..., after 2 years there's .... = ..., etc.

Converting Units

Metric conversions:

1 cm =   **1 tonne =**

1 m =   **1 litre =**

1 km =   **1 litre =**

1 kg =   **1 cm³ =**

Three steps for converting units:

1. **Find**
2.
3. **Choose**

Think which ....

For   **conversions, conversion factors will be given.**

EXAMPLE

Thandi runs 3500 m. How far does she run in km?

1. = ,
   so conversion factor =
2. =
   =
3. =

EXAMPLE

A tank holds 18 gallons of fuel. Given 1 gallon ≈ 4.5 litres, how much fuel can the tank hold in litres?

1. Conversion factor =
2. =
   =
3. ≈

Units — Area, Volume and Time

First Go: ..... /..... /.....

Three Steps for Converting Areas

1. Find the conversion factor for converting ______.
2. Multiply AND divide by it ______.
3. Choose the ______.

① 1 m = 100 cm

②③ $5\ cm^2 = 5 \times$ .... $\times$ ....

= .... m^2

Cross out incorrect working.

$5\ cm^2 = 5 \div$ .... $\div$ ....

= .... m^2

Three Steps for Converting Volumes

1. Find the conversion factor for converting ______.
2. Multiply AND divide by it ______.
3. Choose the ______.

① 1 cm = 10 mm

②③ $2\ cm^3 = 2 \times$ .... $\times$ .... $\times$ ....

= .... mm^3

Cross out incorrect working.

$2\ cm^3 = 2 \div$ .... $\div$ .... $\div$ ....

= .... mm^3

Converting Time Units

Standard time unit conversions:

1 day = ______ **hours**

1 hour = ______ **minutes**

1 minute = ______ **seconds**

EXAMPLE

Write 4800 seconds in hours and minutes.

4800 seconds = 4800 ÷ ______ = ______ minutes

______ minutes = ______ ÷ 60 = 1 full hour

and ______ − 60 = ______ minutes — Split into stages

So 4800 seconds = ______ and ______ minutes

Time Calculations

1. Split ______ into stages.
2. Convert each stage to the ______ (if needed).
3. ______ to get total time.

EXAMPLE

Rowan starts a walk at 10.30 am and finishes at 2.15 pm. How many minutes does his walk last?

① 10.30 am → 11 am → 2 pm → 2.15 pm

______ ______ ______

② 3 hours = 3 × ______ = ______ minutes

③ ______ + ______ + ______ = ______ minutes

Reading Timetables

Here's part of a bus timetable. Read along rows and up/down columns to find answers.

Town Centre	09 50	10 10	10 30
Main Square	09 55	10 15	10 35
Park Avenue	10 03	10 23	10 43

+5 (Town Centre to Main Square), +8 (Main Square to Park Avenue)

First bus from Town Centre gets to Park Avenue at ______.

Town Centre to Park Avenue takes ______.

10:23 bus at Park Avenue leaves Town Centre at ______.

Second Go:
..... /..... /.....

Units — Area, Volume and Time

Three Steps for Converting Areas

1. Find
2.
3. Choose

1. 1 m = ... cm

2. 3. 5 cm^2 = ...

= ....

5 cm^2 = ...

= ....

Three Steps for Converting Volumes

1. Find
2.
3. Choose

1. 1 cm = ... mm

2. 3. 2 cm^3 = ...

= ....

2 cm^3 = ...

= ....

Converting Time Units

Standard time unit conversions:

1 day =

1 hour =

1 minute =

EXAMPLE

Write 4800 seconds in hours and minutes.

4800 seconds = = minutes

minutes = =

and = — Split into stages

So 4800 seconds =

Time Calculations

1. Split
2. Convert each
3. Add

EXAMPLE

Rowan starts a walk at 10.30 am and finishes at 2.15 pm. How many minutes does his walk last?

1. 10.30 am → → → 2.15 pm

2. hours = =

3. =

Reading Timetables

Here's part of a bus timetable. Read along rows and up/down columns to find answers.

First bus from Town Centre gets to Park Avenue at .

Town Centre	09 50	10 10	10 30
Main Square	09 55	10 15	10 35
Park Avenue	10 03	10 23	10 43

Town Centre to Park Avenue takes .

10:23 bus at leaves Town Centre at .

Speed, Density and Pressure

First Go: ...../...../.....

Speed, Time and Distance

SPEED = ________

TIME = ________

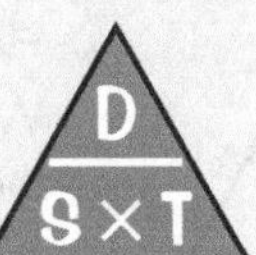

DISTANCE = ×

Units of speed: distance travelled per unit time, e.g. ,

EXAMPLE

A fox walks 13.5 km at an average speed of 4.5 km/h. How long does the fox walk for?

Write down the formula: Time = ________

Put in the numbers: = ______

Add the units: =

In a formula triangle, ... and write what's left.

Density, Volume and Mass

DENSITY = ________

VOLUME = ________

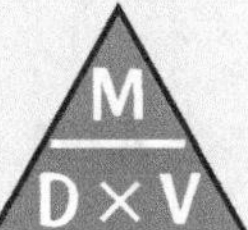

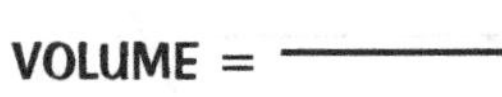

MASS = ×

Units of density: mass per unit volume, e.g. ,

Pressure, Area and Force

PRESSURE = ________

AREA = ________

FORCE = ×

Units of pressure: force per unit area, e.g. (or)

Converting Units of Speed, Density and Pressure

Units of speed, density and pressure are made up of .

Convert each .

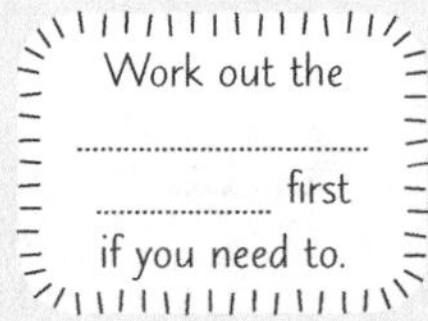

Work out the .... first if you need to.

EXAMPLE

Convert 300 m/s to km/h.

Cross out incorrect working.

300 m/s to km/s:

1 km = ... m, so conversion factor = ...

300 × .... = ..., 300 ÷ .... = ...

So 300 m/s = ... km/s

...... km/s to km/h:

1 h = ... mins and 1 min = ... s,

so conversion factor = ... × ...... = ...

0.3 × .... = ..., 0.3 ÷ .... = ...

So 300 m/s = ... km/s = ... km/h

Second Go:
...... /...... /......

Speed, Density and Pressure

Speed, Time and Distance

SPEED = ——————

TIME = ——————

DISTANCE = ×

Units of speed:
per , e.g. ,

EXAMPLE

A fox walks 13.5 km at an average speed of 4.5 km/h. How long does the fox walk for?

Write down the formula: =

Put in the numbers: =

Add the units: =

In a formula triangle, ...
....

Density, Volume and Mass

DENSITY = ——————

VOLUME = ——————

MASS = ×

Units of density: per
, e.g. ,

Pressure, Area and Force

PRESSURE = ——————

AREA = ——————

FORCE = ×

Units of pressure: per
area, e.g. (or)

Converting Units of Speed, Density and Pressure

Units of speed, density and pressure are
.

Convert
.

Work out ....
....
....
if you need to.

EXAMPLE

Convert 300 m/s to km/h.

Cross out incorrect working.

300 m/s to km/s:
1 km = ..., so conversion factor = ...

So 300 m/s = ...

.... km/s to km/h:
1 h = ... and 1 min = ...,
so conversion factor = ... = ...

So 300 m/s = ... = ...

Mixed Practice Quizzes

Make sure you're up to speed by testing yourself on everything from p.75-84.
Have a go at the questions, then mark your answers — fun 100% guaranteed.

Quiz 1

Date: ...... / ...... / ......

1) How do you find 10% of a number?
2) Annie leaves home at 10:45 am. She gets back at 12:15 pm. How long does she spend out of the house in hours and minutes?
3) How do you convert between metres and kilometres?
4) What is the first step in writing 18 as a percentage of 54?
5) What multiplier would you use to find the new value after a 15% decrease?
6) £28 is 80% of a jumper's original price. What is the next step to find the original price of the jumper?
7) How would you convert cm^3 into m^3?
8) What is the formula for compound growth and decay?
9) How many seconds are there in 5 minutes?
10) What is the formula for pressure?

Total:

Quiz 2

Date: ...... / ...... / ......

1) The bill in a restaurant is £40. A tip of 10% is added to the bill. What is the value of the tip?
2) How would you convert one hour into seconds?
3) How do you write one number as a percentage of another number?
4) What does N_0 represent in the compound growth formula?
5) Is depreciation an example of compound growth or compound decay?
6) Given a force in N and area in m^2, what would the unit for pressure be?
7) How many times do you need to multiply or divide by the conversion factor when converting an area into different units?
8) What formula would you use to calculate time, given speed and distance?
9) What is 4.3 litres in millilitres?
10) What is the formula for finding the percentage change?

Total:

Mixed Practice Quizzes

Quiz 3

Date: ...... / ...... / ......

1) How many kilograms are in one tonne?
2) What is the formula for speed?
3) What is the first step in finding a percentage of an amount?
4) What is the formula triangle for density, mass and volume?
5) What multiplier would you use to find the new value after a 25% increase?
6) Given 1 kg ≈ 2.2 pounds, what is 5 kg in pounds?
7) What is the first step in using the percentage change formula to calculate a percentage loss?
8) How would you find the interest earned from an account paying 2% simple interest over 3 years?
9) What is 3 hours 25 minutes in minutes?
10) What is the first step to find the original value after a percentage change?

Total:

Quiz 4

Date: ...... / ...... / ......

1) What is 1% of 1200?
2) What is the conversion factor between metres and centimetres?
3) Give two methods to calculate the new amount after a percentage change.
4) An account contains £5000 and earns 5% compound interest each year. What would the multiplier be when using the compound growth formula?
5) How many grams are in one kilogram?
6) A cube with a base area of 4 m^2 applies a force of 800 N to the ground. What is the pressure exerted by the cube?
7) A runner has an average speed of 8 km/h. How far would they run in 45 minutes?
8) What is simple interest?
9) How do you convert from cm^2 into mm^2?
10) Jenny buys a vase for £25. She sells it and makes £5 profit. What is her percentage profit?

Total:

Properties of 2D Shapes

First Go: ..... /..... /.....

Line Symmetry

LINE SYMMETRY — where the of a shape on either side of a mirror line exactly together.

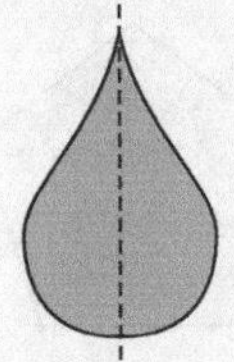

line of symmetry

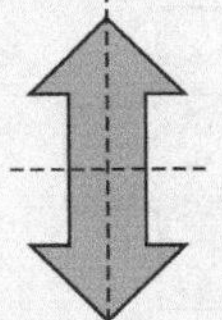

lines of symmetry

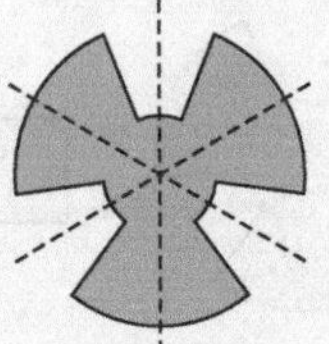

lines of symmetry

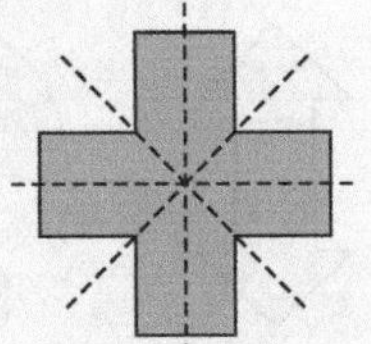

lines of symmetry

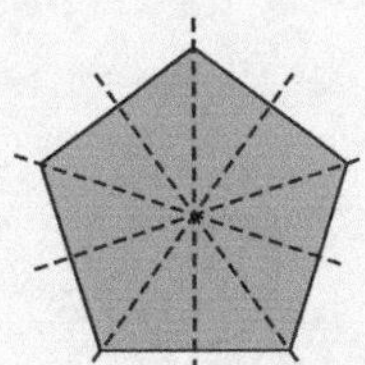

lines of symmetry

Rotational Symmetry

ROTATIONAL SYMMETRY — where a shape looks after you rotate it into .

ORDER OF ROTATIONAL SYMMETRY — how many different positions .

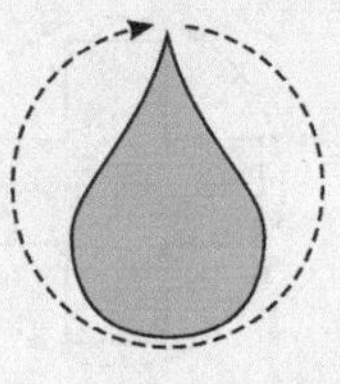

Order

Same as rotational symmetry.

Order

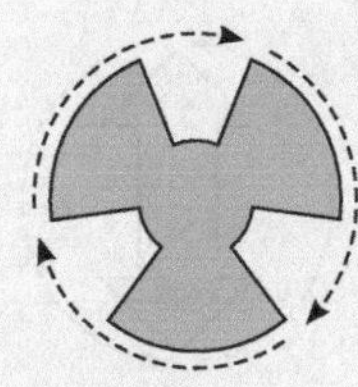

Order

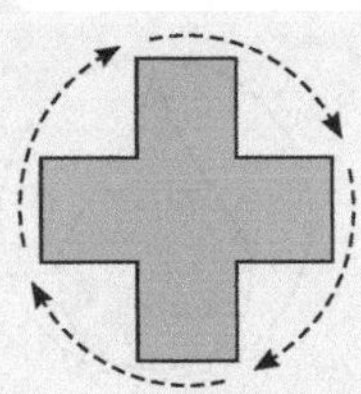

Order

Regular Polygons

REGULAR POLYGON — all and are the same.

Equilateral triangles and squares are .... polygons.

Name	**Pentagon**			**Octagon**	**Nonagon**	
No. of sides		**6**	**7**	**8**		**10**

Regular polygons have the same number of lines of symmetry as the number of .
Their order of is also the same.

Second Go:
...../...../.....

Properties of 2D Shapes

Line Symmetry

LINE SYMMETRY —

Draw the lines of symmetry for these shapes.

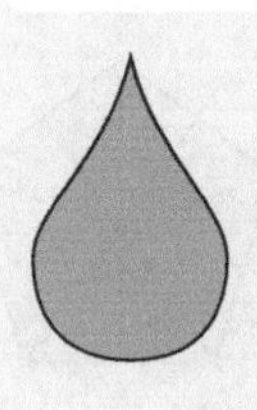

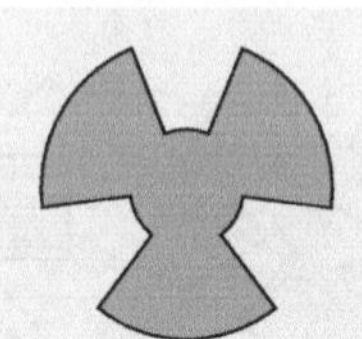
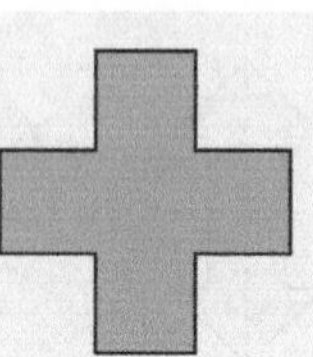

______ of symmetry	______ of symmetry	______ of symmetry	______ of symmetry	______ of symmetry

Rotational Symmetry

ROTATIONAL SYMMETRY —

ORDER OF ROTATIONAL SYMMETRY —

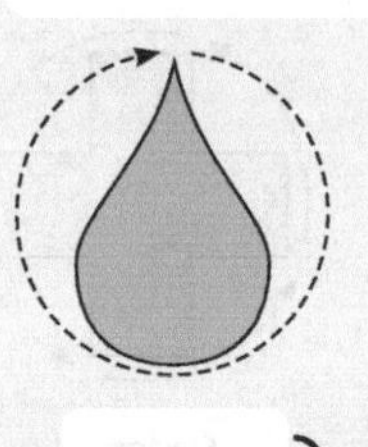
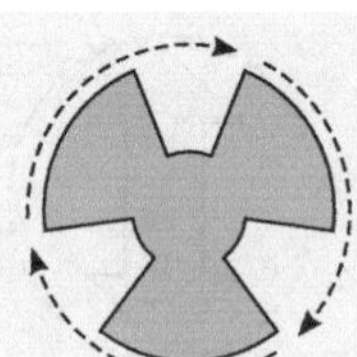
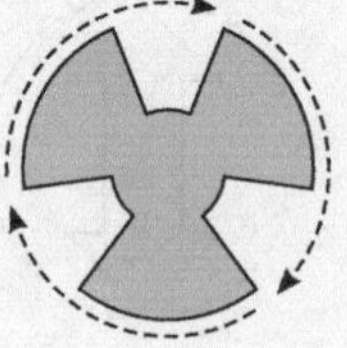
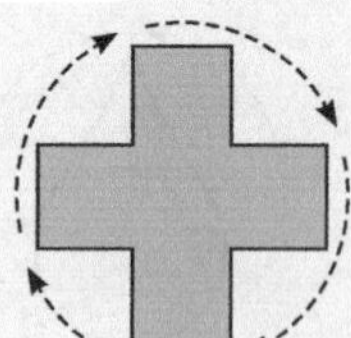

Same as ______.

Regular Polygons

REGULAR POLYGON —

.... triangles and .... are regular polygons.

Name	**Pentagon**			**Octagon**		
No. of sides			**7**			

Regular polygons have the same ______ as the ______. Their ______ is also the same.

Triangles and Quadrilaterals

First Go: ...../...../.....

Four Types of Triangles

All sides and angles are ....

Dashes show sides of the same length.

60°

90°

Type	Equilateral	Isosceles	Right-angled	
Lines of symmetry		1	0 (unless isosceles)	0
Rotational symmetry	Order 3			None

Six Types of Quadrilaterals

SQUARE

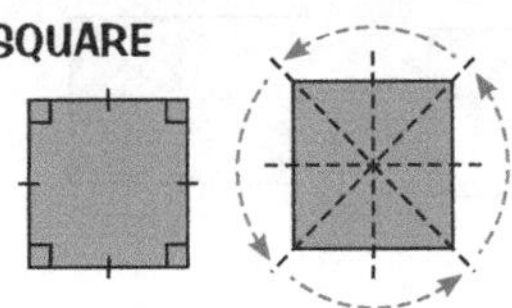

- 4 equal angles of ....°
- .... of symmetry
- Rotational symmetry order ....

RECTANGLE

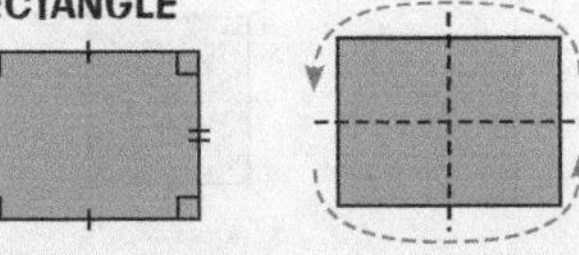

- 4 equal angles of °
- of symmetry
- Rotational symmetry order

RHOMBUS

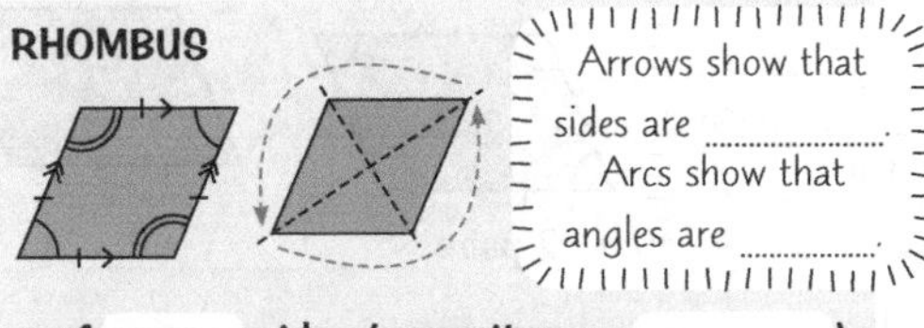

Arrows show that sides are ....

Arcs show that angles are ....

- 4 sides (opposites are)
- 2 pairs of
- of symmetry
- Rotational symmetry order

PARALLELOGRAM

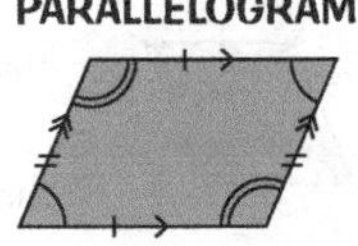

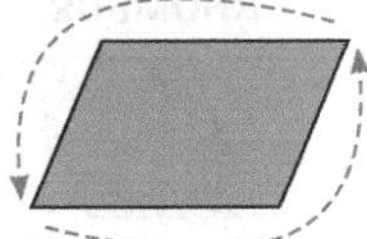

- .... pairs of equal sides (sides in each pair are ....)
- .... of equal angles
- .... of symmetry
- Rotational symmetry order ....

TRAPEZIUM

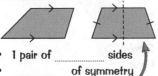

- 1 pair of .... sides
- .... of symmetry (unless ....)
- .... rotational symmetry

KITE

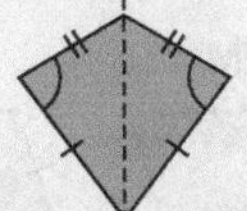

- pairs of equal sides
- 1 pair of angles
- of symmetry
- rotational symmetry

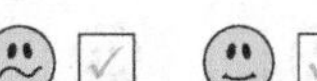

Second Go: ...../...../.....

Triangles and Quadrilaterals

Four Types of Triangles

.... are different.

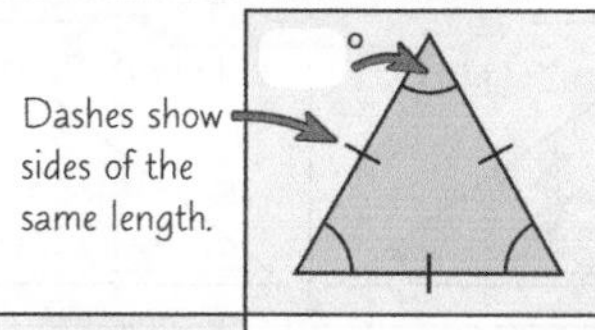
Dashes show sides of the same length.

Type		Isosceles		Scalene
Lines of symmetry			(unless isosceles)	
Rotational symmetry				

Six Types of Quadrilaterals

SQUARE

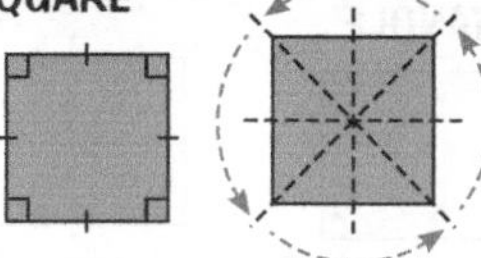

- 4 ....
- 4 ....
- ....

RECTANGLE

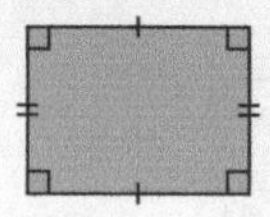
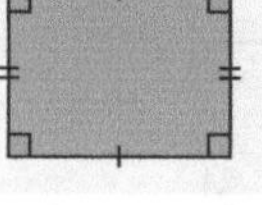

- 4
- 2
-

RHOMBUS

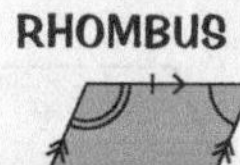
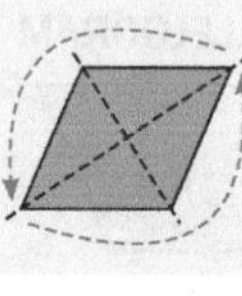
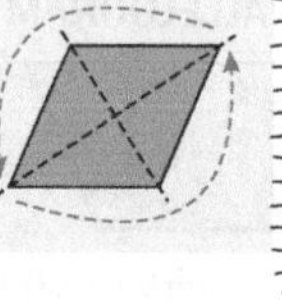
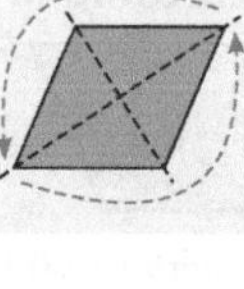

Arrows show that .... Arcs show that ....

- 4 ( )
- 2 pairs
- 2
-

PARALLELOGRAM

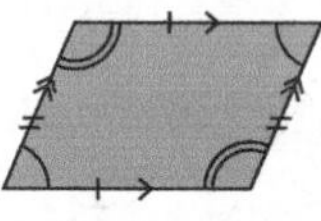
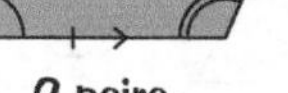
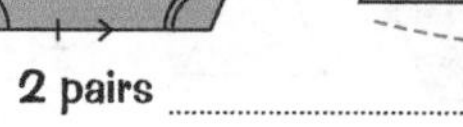

- 2 pairs .... (................................)
- 2 pairs ....
- No ....
- ....

TRAPEZIUM

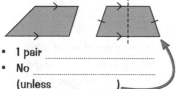

- 1 pair ....
- No .... (unless ....)
- ....

KITE

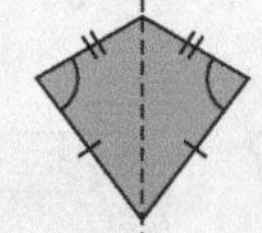

- 2 pairs
- 1 pair
- 1
-

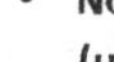

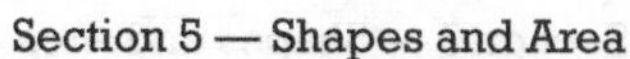

Congruent and Similar Shapes

First Go:
..... / ..... / .....

Congruent Shapes

CONGRUENT — .... **size and** .... **shape.**

EXAMPLE

Which of these shapes are congruent?

✓ ✓ ✓ ✓ ✗

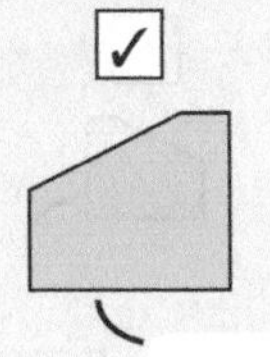
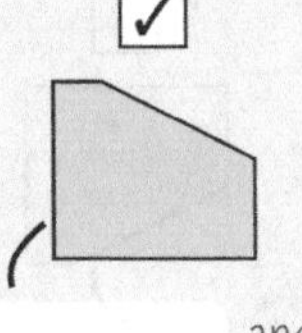
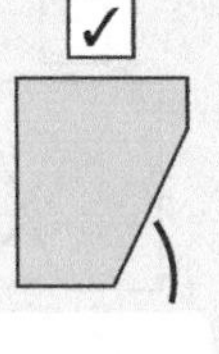
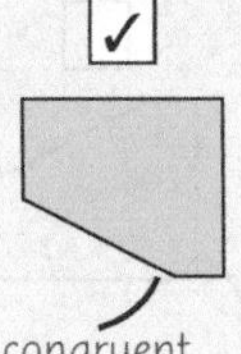
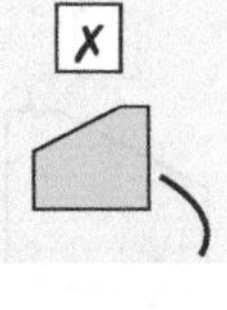

and are congruent. , so not congruent.

Four Conditions for Congruent Triangles

Condition	1 SSS	2 ASA	3	4 RHS
Description	three the same	two and corresponding side match up	two sides and angle them match up	angle, hypotenuse and another side all match up
Diagrams				

Similar Shapes

SIMILAR — **shape,** **size.**

If you know two shapes are ...., work out the .... to find any missing lengths.

Three conditions for similar triangles:

 **All** **match up.**

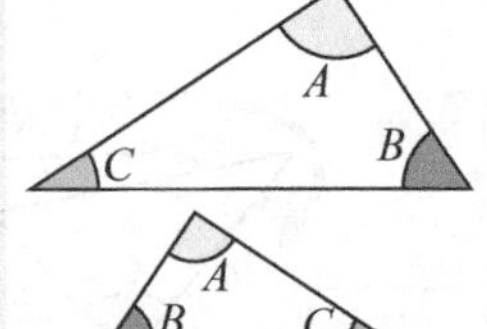

 **All sides are** .

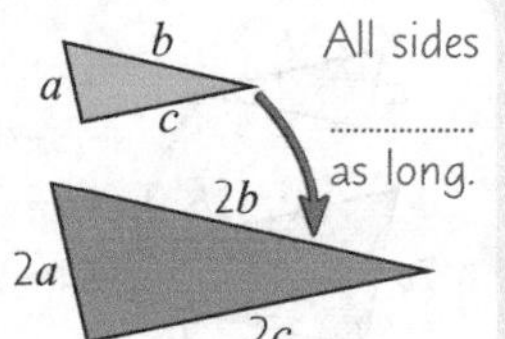

 **Two sides proportional and the** **between them is the same.**

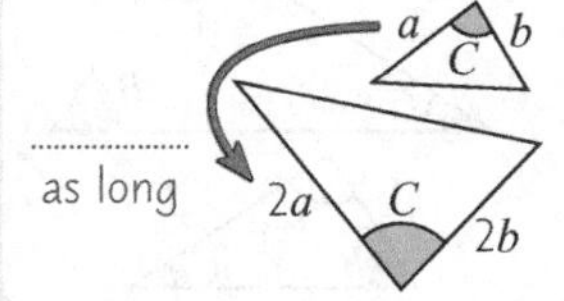

Second Go: ...../...../.....

Congruent and Similar Shapes

Congruent Shapes

CONGRUENT — ....

EXAMPLE Which of these shapes are congruent?

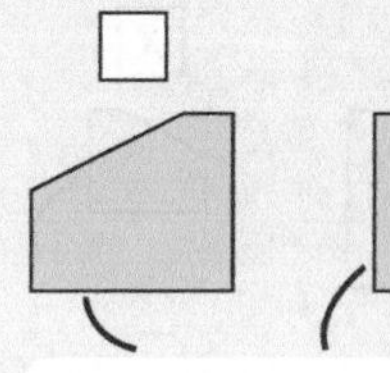
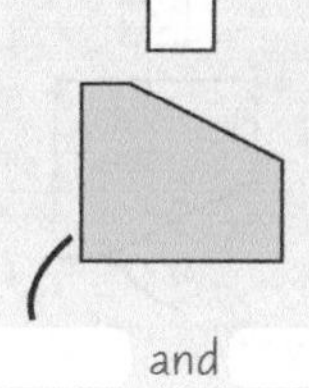
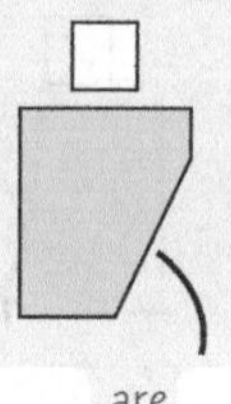
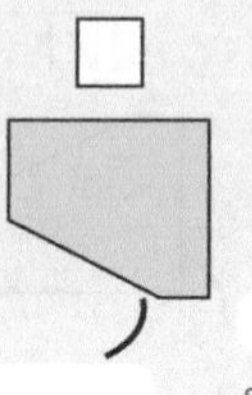
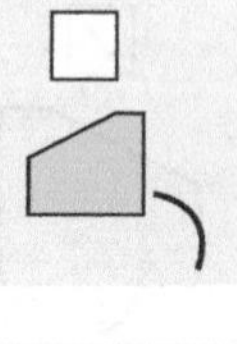

and are . so ,.

Four Conditions for Congruent Triangles

Condition	1	2	3	4
Description				
Diagrams				

Similar Shapes

SIMILAR — .

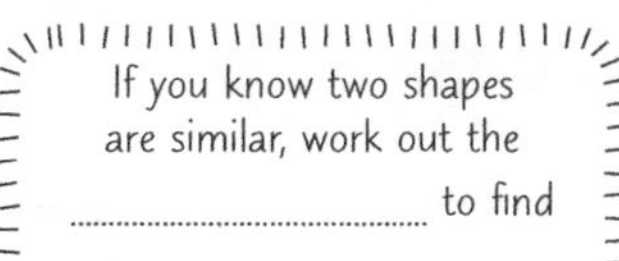

If you know two shapes are similar, work out the .... to find ....

Three conditions for similar triangles:

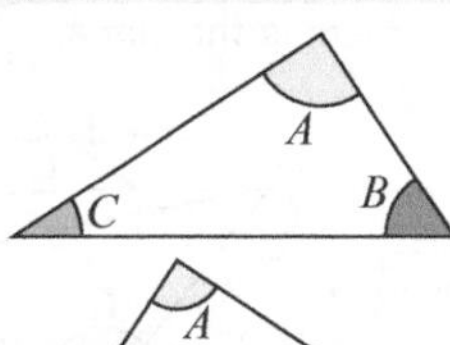

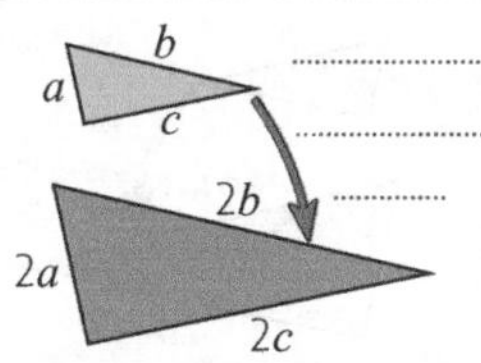

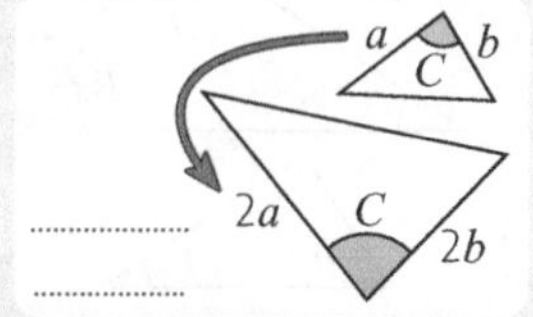

The Four Transformations

First Go: ..... /..... /.....

Translation

Amount a shape moves is given by $\begin{pmatrix} x \\ y \end{pmatrix}$.

x = horizontal movement (+ , –)

y = vertical movement (+ , –)

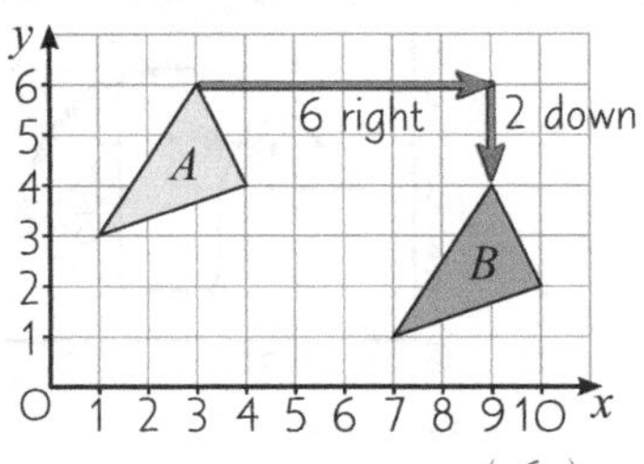

Translation from A to B: $\begin{pmatrix} 6 \\ \ldots \end{pmatrix}$

Rotation

To describe a rotation you need:

1. the angle
2. the
3. the of rotation

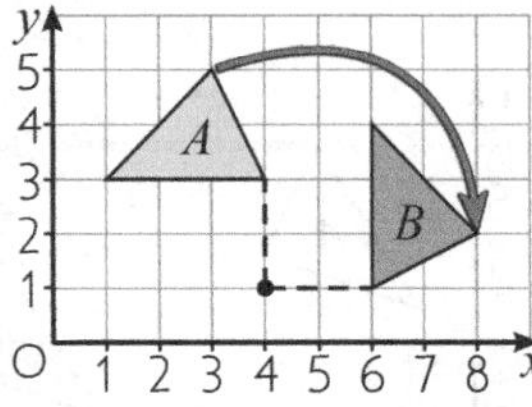

Rotation from A to B:

90° .... about (4, 1)

Reflection

Describe by giving the equation of the .

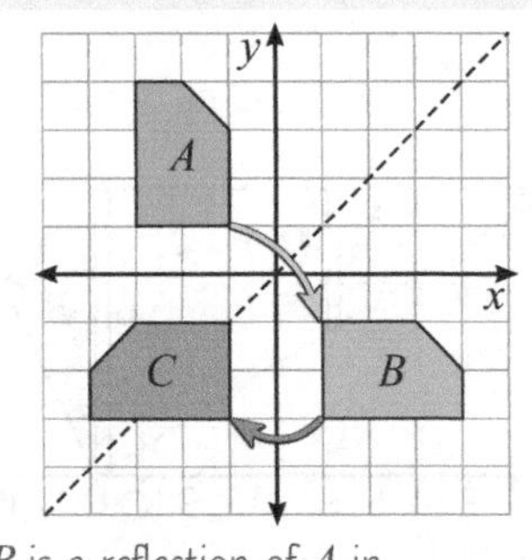

B is a reflection of A in ....

C is a reflection of ..... in the y-axis

Enlargement

To describe an enlargement you need:

1. the = $\frac{\text{new length}}{\text{old length}}$
2. the of enlargement

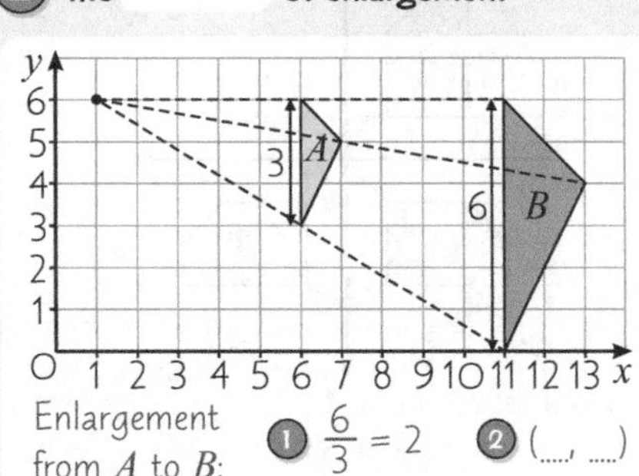

Enlargement from A to B: ① $\frac{6}{3} = 2$ ② (....., ...)

Three Facts about Scale Factors

1. If than 1, shape gets bigger (e.g. 2).
2. If between , shape gets smaller (e.g. $\frac{1}{2}$).
3. They give the relative distance of the new and old points from the .

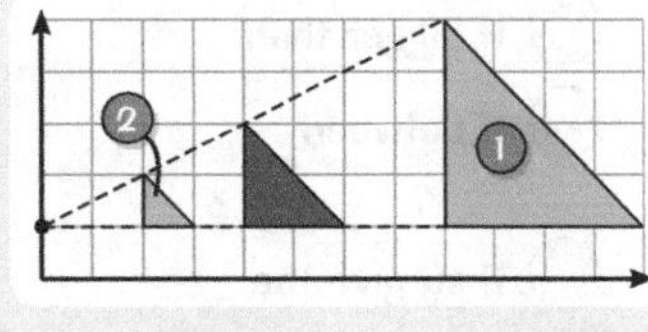

Second Go:
..... /..... /.....

The Four Transformations

Translation

Amount a shape moves is given by .

x =

y =

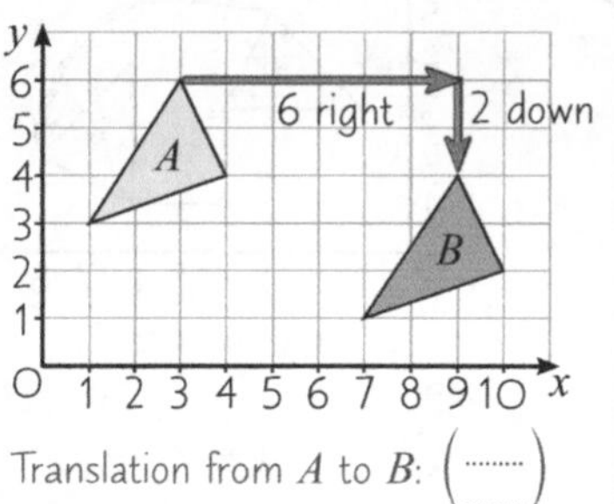

Rotation

To describe a rotation you need:

1 2

3

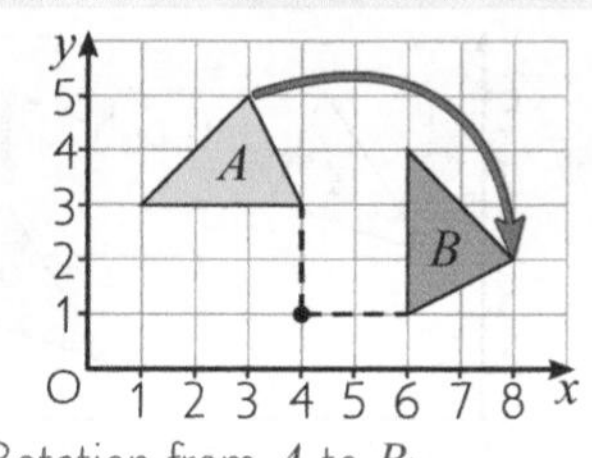

Reflection

Describe by giving the .

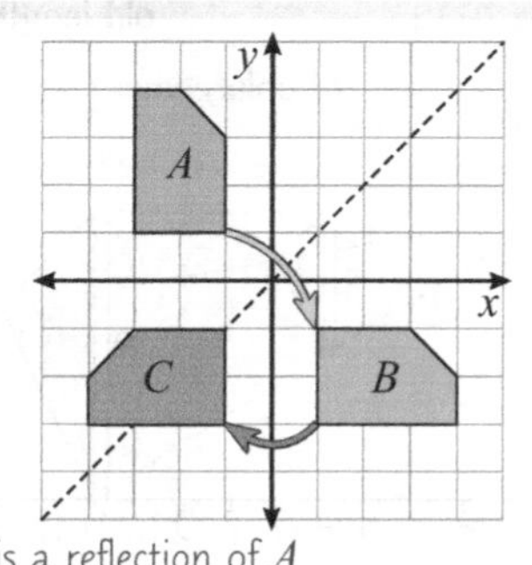

Enlargement

To describe an enlargement you need:

1

2

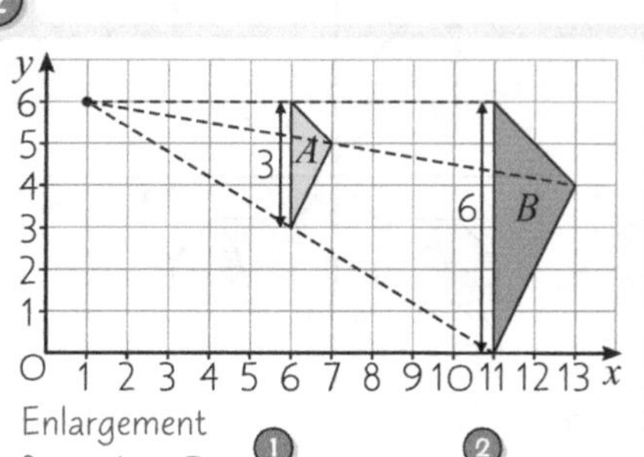

Three Facts about Scale Factors

1 If bigger than (e.g. 2).

2 If between (e.g. $\frac{1}{2}$).

3 They give the of the from the .

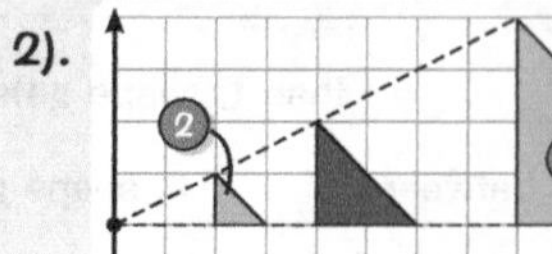

Mixed Practice Quizzes

So to summarise, symmetry and similarity are super significant. So is songru- sorry, congruence. All that and the rest of p.87-94 are covered in these quizzes.

Quiz 1

Date: ...... / ...... / ......

1) True or false? A rectangle has 4 equal angles of 60°.
2) What does the congruence condition SSS mean?
3) In a vector describing a translation, does the top or bottom number show the horizontal movement?
4) True or false? Two triangles are similar if two sides are proportional and the angle between them is the same.
5) What is a regular polygon?
6) What is the formula for the scale factor of an enlargement?
7) What is the order of rotational symmetry of the letter W?
8) How many pairs of parallel sides does a trapezium have?
9) (1, 5) is reflected in the x-axis. What are the coordinates of the new point?
10) How many lines of symmetry does an equilateral triangle have?

Total:

Quiz 2

Date: ...... / ...... / ......

1) What are congruent shapes?
2) What is the order of rotational symmetry of a multiplication sign (×)?
3) The scale factor for an enlargement is between 0 and 1. What happens to the shape?
4) How many lines of symmetry does a kite have?
5) Square A is 3 cm wide. Square B is 5 cm wide. Are A and B similar?
6) How many pairs of parallel sides does a parallelogram have?
7) What is line symmetry?
8) If you know that two angles match in each of two triangles, what else do you need to show they are congruent?
9) What size are the angles in an equilateral triangle?
10) What three pieces of information do you need to describe a rotation?

Total:

Mixed Practice Quizzes

Quiz 3

Date: ...... / ...... / ......

1) What two pieces of information do you need to describe an enlargement?
2) How many sides does an octagon have?
3) True or false? A shape and its mirror image are congruent.
4) A shape is rotated 90° with a centre of (2, 3).
   What else do you need to fully describe the rotation?
5) Which quadrilateral has no line symmetry and rotational symmetry order 2?
6) How many lines of symmetry does a division sign (÷) have?
7) In which type of triangle are all sides and angles different?
8) What are the four different conditions for congruent triangles?
9) When spun around, a shape only looks the same when upside down and when back to its starting position. What is its order of rotational symmetry?
10) A translation is given by $\begin{pmatrix} 3 \\ -2 \end{pmatrix}$. Describe the movement of the shape.

Total:

Quiz 4

Date: ...... / ...... / ......

1) How many pairs of equal angles does a rhombus have?
2) How many different pieces of information do you need to show that two triangles are congruent?
3) How many lines of symmetry does a regular nonagon have?
4) What information do you need to describe a reflection?
5) Which type of triangle is a regular polygon?
6) What is the order of rotational symmetry of a shape with no rotational symmetry?
7) True or false? You can tell that two triangles are congruent if two sides and any angle match up.
8) The enlargement of shape X to Y has scale factor 3. A point on X is 6 units from the centre of enlargement. How far is the point on Y from the centre?
9) Two triangles are similar if all their sides are what?
10) How many lines of symmetry does an isosceles trapezium have?

Total:

Perimeter and Area

First Go: ..... /..... /.....

Triangles and Quadrilaterals

PERIMETER — distance around the of a shape.

AREA — by a shape.

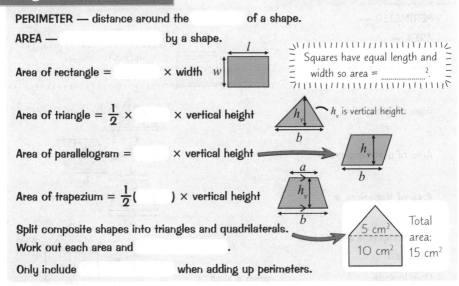

Area of rectangle = × width

Squares have equal length and width so area = ...^{2}.

Area of triangle = $\frac{1}{2}$ × × vertical height

h_v is vertical height.

Area of parallelogram = × vertical height

Area of trapezium = $\frac{1}{2}$( ) × vertical height

Split composite shapes into triangles and quadrilaterals.

Work out each area and .

Only include when adding up perimeters.

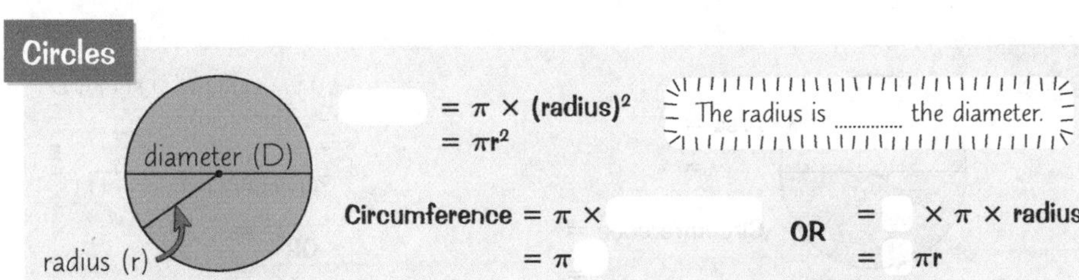

Circles

= π × (radius)^2
= πr^2

The radius is .... the diameter.

diameter (D)

radius (r)

Circumference = π × = π

OR = × π × radius = πr

Arcs and Sectors

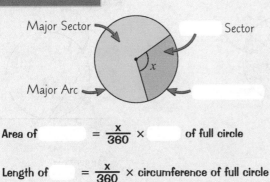

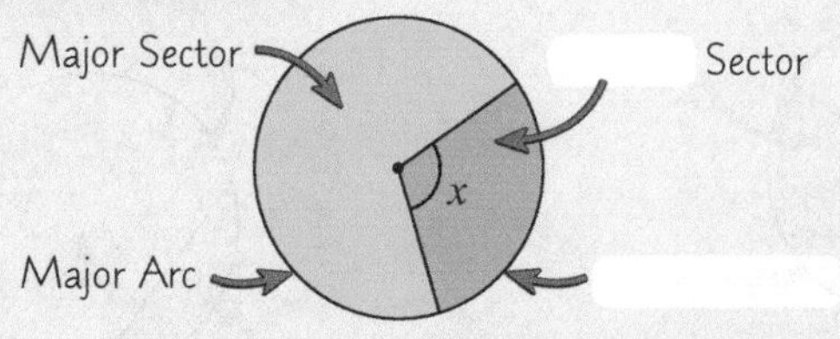

Area of = $\frac{x}{360}$ × of full circle

Length of = $\frac{x}{360}$ × circumference of full circle

Segments

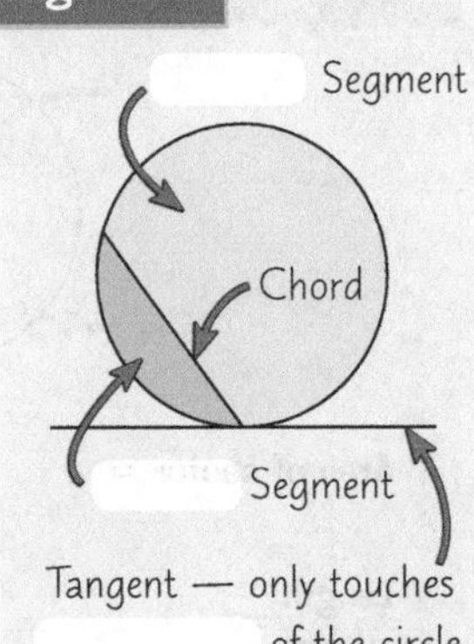

Tangent — only touches of the circle

Second Go:
...../...../.....

Perimeter and Area

Triangles and Quadrilaterals

PERIMETER — .

AREA — .

Area of rectangle =

Squares have equal .... and .... so area = ...

Area of triangle =

h_v is vertical height.

Area of parallelogram =

Area of trapezium =

Split composite shapes into .
Work out .
Only include **when adding up** .

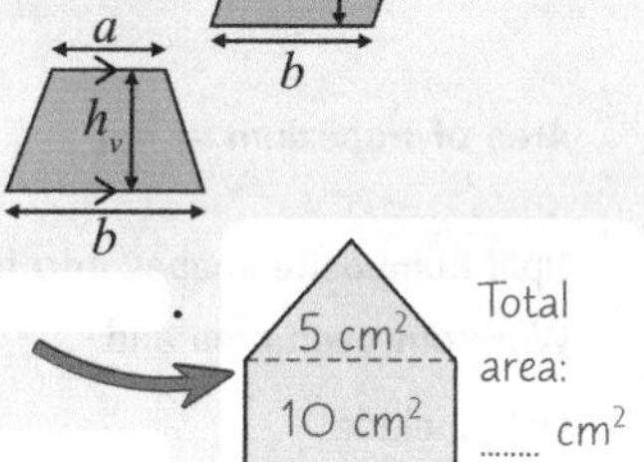

Circles

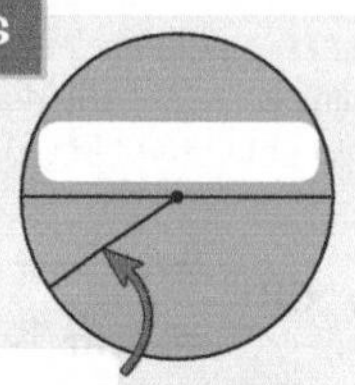

Area =
=

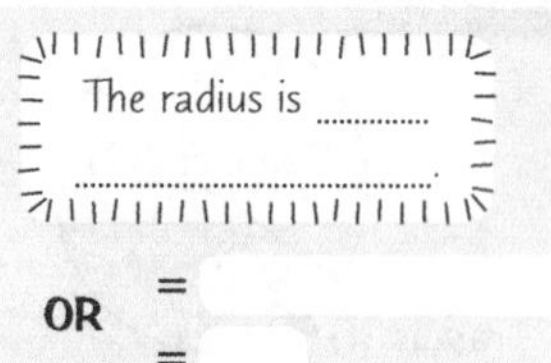

Circumference =
=

OR =
=

Arcs and Sectors

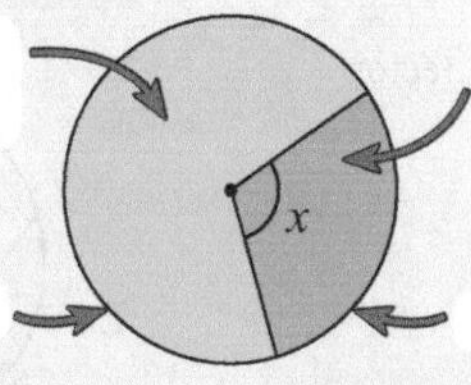

Area of sector =

Length of arc =

Segments

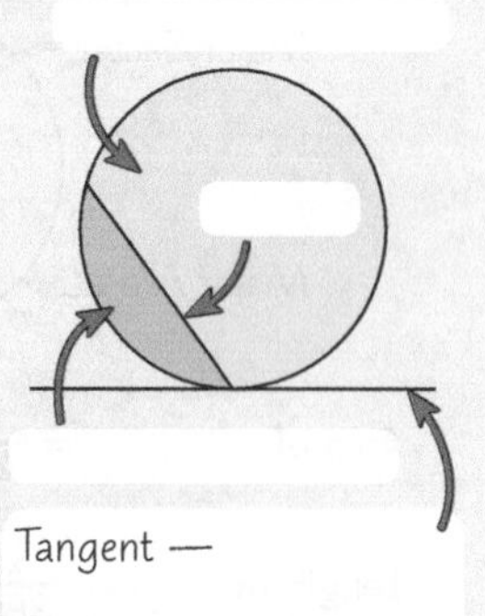

Tangent —

3D Shapes

First Go: ..... /..... /.....

Eight 3D Shapes

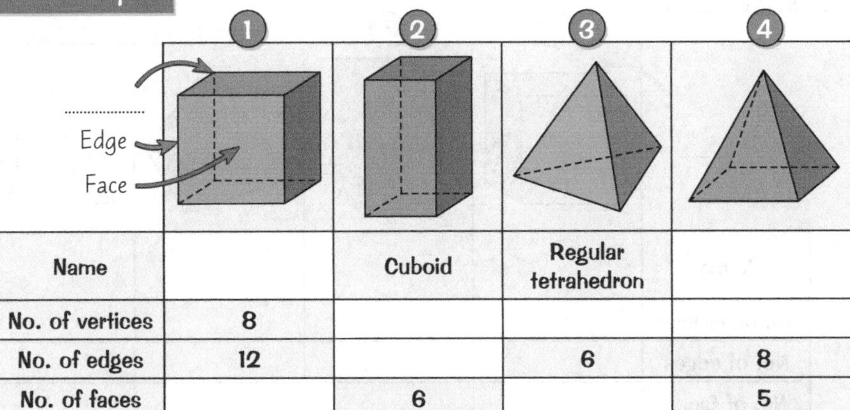

Name		Cuboid	Regular tetrahedron	
No. of vertices	8			
No. of edges	12		6	8
No. of faces		6		5

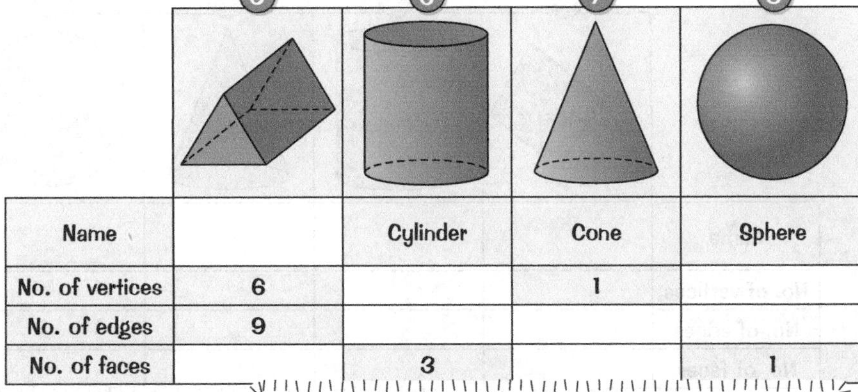

Name		Cylinder	Cone	Sphere
No. of vertices	6		1	
No. of edges	9			
No. of faces		3		1

Faces (especially curved ones) may also be called ....

Three Projections

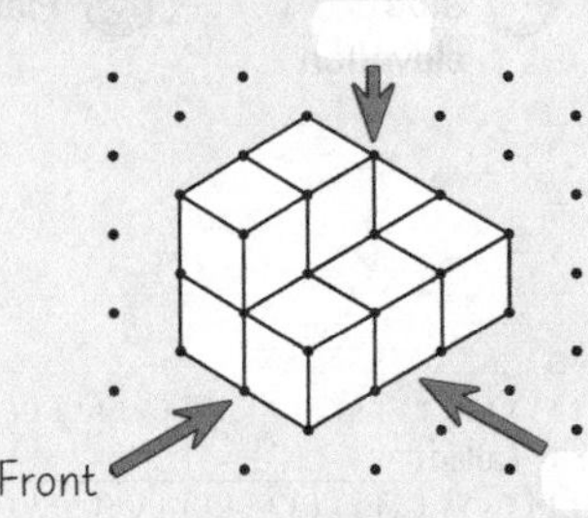

1 Front elevation

2 elevation

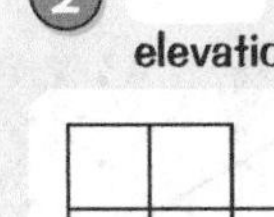

3

The dotty paper is called .... paper.

Second Go:
..... /..... /.....

3D Shapes

Eight 3D Shapes

....
....
....

	1	2	3	4
Name				
No. of vertices				
No. of edges				
No. of faces				

	5	6	7	8
Name				
No. of vertices				
No. of edges				
No. of faces				

Faces (especially ....) may also be called ....

Three Projections

1 Front elevation

2 Side elevation

3 Plan

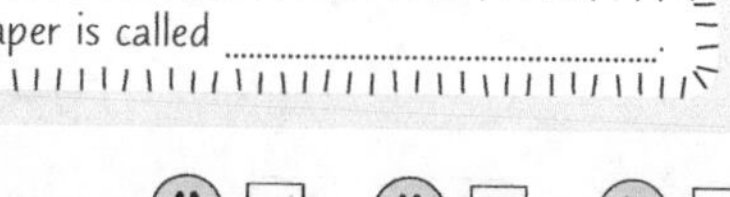
The dotty paper is called ....

Surface Area and Volume

First Go: ..... /..... /.....

Surface Area Using Nets

SURFACE AREA — total area of all .

NET — a folded out flat.

Surface area of solid = ... of net

EXAMPLE

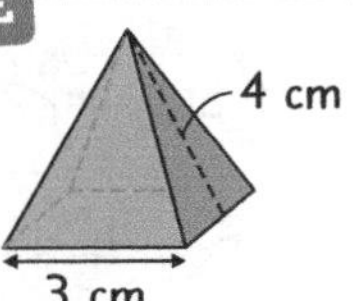

Sketch the net of the pyramid.

4 cm

3 cm

1 square face, 4 triangular faces

Area of square face = ... × ..... = ... cm^2

Area of triangular face = $\frac{1}{2}$ × ..... × ..... = ... cm^2

Total surface area = ... + (..................) = 9 + 24 = ... cm^2

Surface Area Formulas

Surface area of sphere =

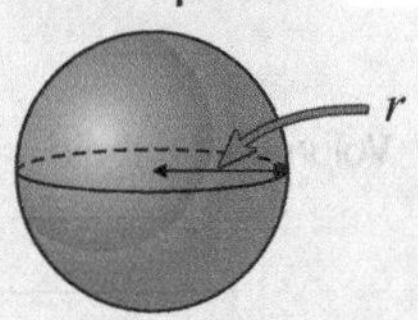

Surface area of cone = πrl +

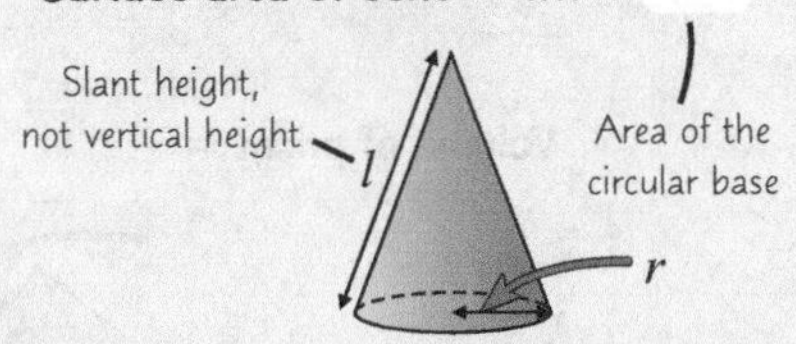

Surface area of cylinder = + 2πr²

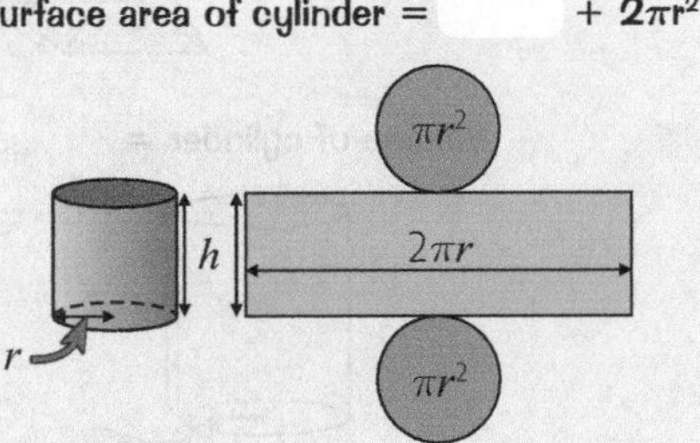

Volumes of Cuboids and Prisms

VOLUME — a 3D shape.

Volume of cuboid = × ×

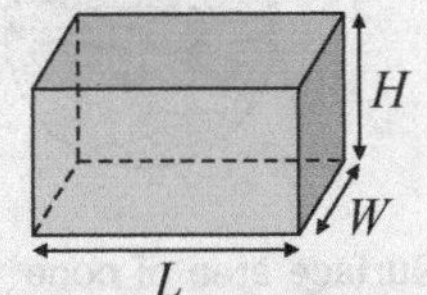

Volume of prism = A ×

A = constant of cross-section

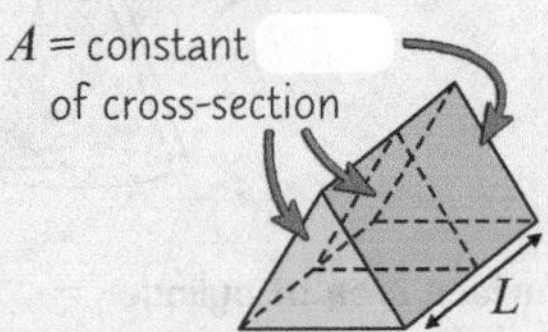

Volume of cylinder =

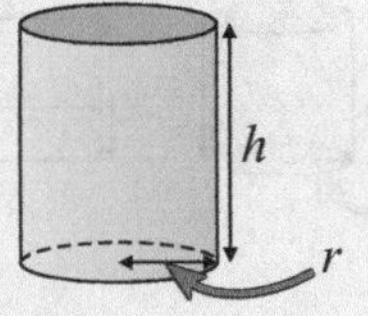

Second Go:
...../...../.....

Surface Area and Volume

Surface Area Using Nets

SURFACE AREA — .

NET — .

Surface area of solid
= ....

EXAMPLE

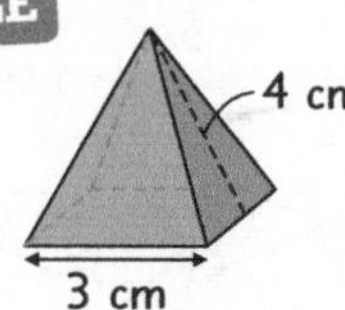

Sketch the net of the pyramid.

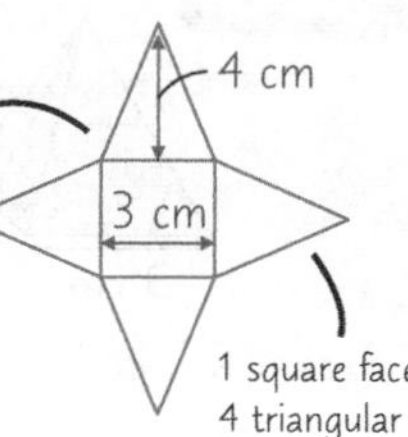

Area of square face = ... = ...

Area of triangular face = ... = ...

Total surface area = ... = ... = ...

Surface Area Formulas

Surface area of sphere =

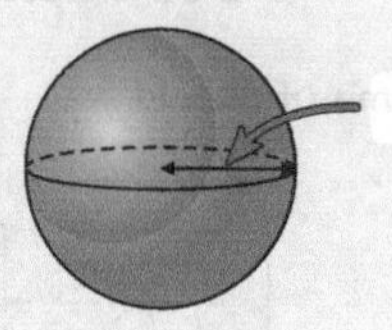

Surface area of cone =

Slant height,
not vertical height

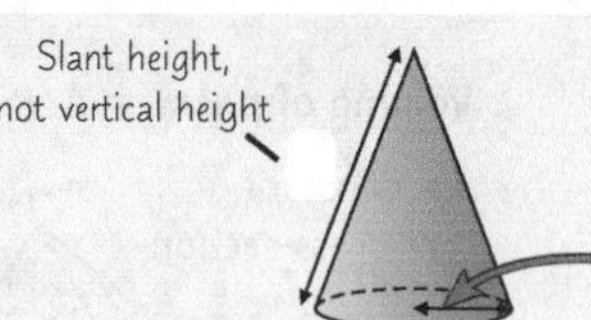

Surface area of cylinder =

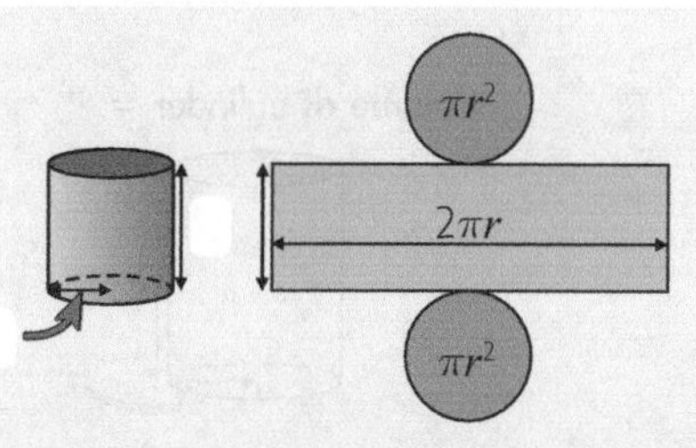

Volumes of Cuboids and Prisms

VOLUME —

Volume of cuboid =

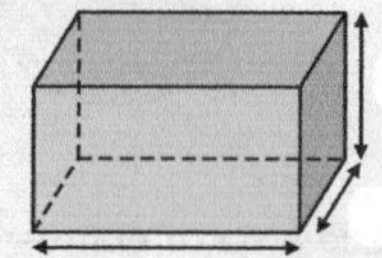

Volume of prism =

A =

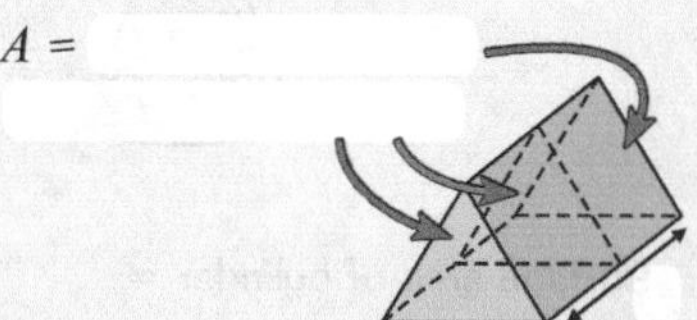

Volume of cylinder =

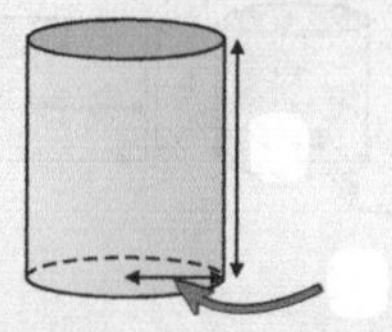

Volume

First Go: ..... /..... /.....

Other Volume Formulas

Volume of sphere
$= \frac{4}{3}\pi$

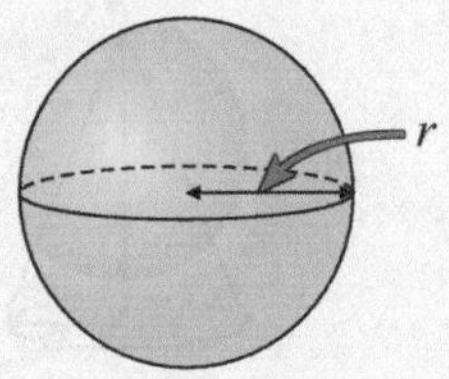

Volume of pyramid
$= \frac{1}{3} \times$ base area $\times$

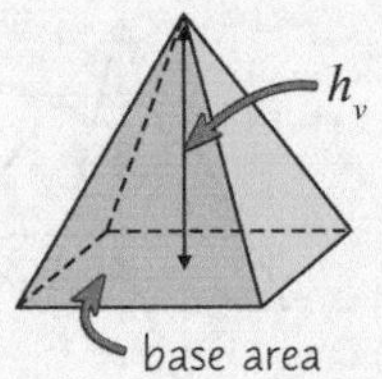

Volume of cone
$= \quad \pi r^2 h_v$

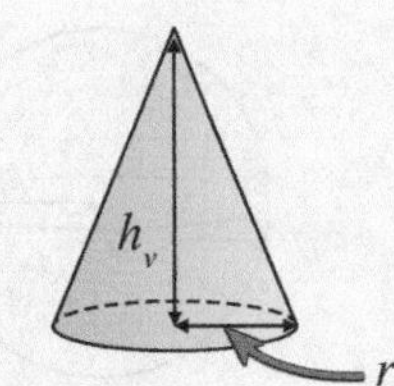

Volume of frustum = volume of cone
– volume of cone
$= \frac{1}{3}\pi R^2 H - \frac{1}{3}\pi$

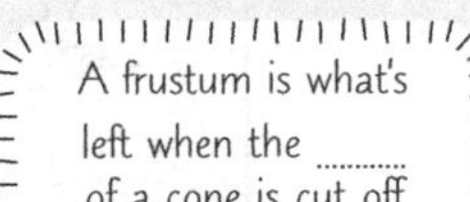

A frustum is what's left when the .... of a cone is cut off .... to its base.

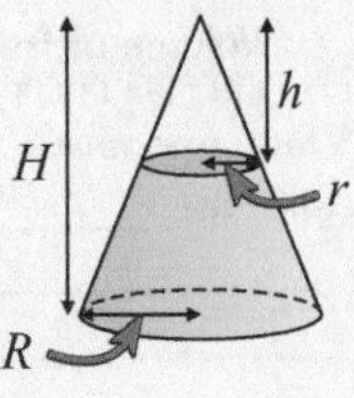

Two Steps for Ratios of Volumes

To show how the of shapes are linked, find the of their volumes:

1. Work out each separately and make sure they are in the .
2. Write the volumes as a and simplify.

EXAMPLE

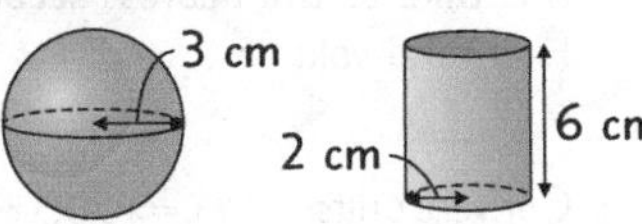

1. Volume of sphere = ... = ...π cm^3

   Volume of cylinder = $\pi r^2 h$ = ...π cm^3

2. Sphere : cylinder = ...:.......... = ...:.....

Rates of Flow

RATE OF FLOW — how fast is changing.

The of shapes are often given in units to the rate of flow.

EXAMPLE

A cylinder with radius 10 cm and height 8 cm is filled with water at 1 litre per minute. How long does this take to the nearest second?

Find total volume:
V = π × .... × ...... = 2513.2... cm^3

Convert units: 1 L = 1000 cm^3
1 L/min × 1000 = 1000 ..../.........
1000 cm^3/min ÷ 60 = 16.6... ..../......

Solve for time:
2513.2... ÷ .... = 151 s (to nearest s)

Second Go: ...../...../.....

Volume

Other Volume Formulas

Volume of sphere =

Volume of pyramid =

Volume of cone =

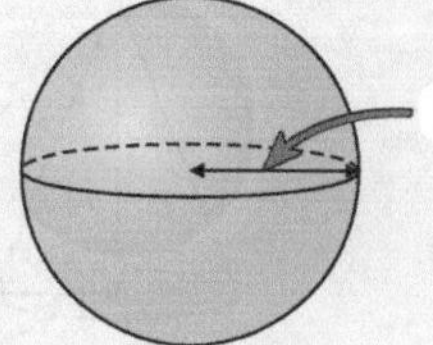

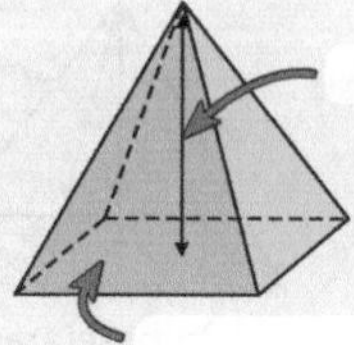

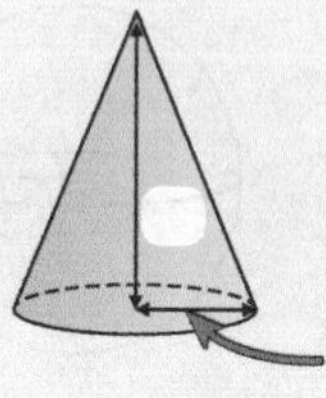

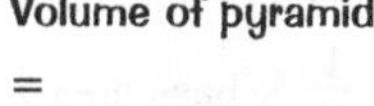

Volume of frustum =

−

= −

A frustum is what's left when the ....

Two Steps for Ratios of Volumes

To show how the are linked, find the :

1. Work out and make sure .
2. Write the volumes .

EXAMPLE

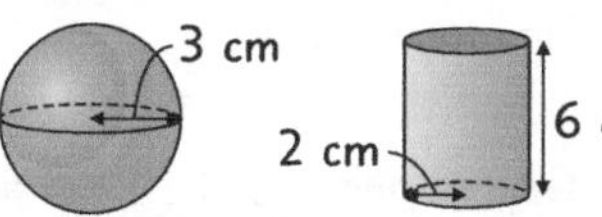

1. Volume of sphere = ... = ...

   Volume of cylinder = ... = ...

2. Sphere : cylinder = ... = ...

Rates of Flow

RATE OF FLOW —

The are often given in to the .

EXAMPLE

A cylinder with radius 10 cm and height 8 cm is filled with water at 1 litre per minute. How long does this take to the nearest second?

Find total volume:

V = ... = ...

Convert units: 1 L = 1000 cm^3

1 L/min × .... = ... cm^3/min

.... cm^3/min ÷ ...... = ... cm^3/s

Solve for time:

.... = ...

(to nearest s)

Mixed Practice Quizzes

Are you ambivalent to area? Or frustrated by frustums? You won't be after practising with these quizzes covering p.97-104. Remember to add up your scores.

Quiz 1

Date: ...... / ...... / ......

1) True or false? A cube and a cuboid have the same number of edges.
2) What is volume?
3) Which type of projection shows the view from above?
4) What is the formula for the volume of a pyramid?
5) How many vertices, edges and faces does a regular tetrahedron have?
6) What is the formula for the length of an arc of angle x?
7) What is the area of a triangle with base 2 cm and vertical height 3 cm?
8) How do you find the volume of a frustum?
9) What is the perimeter of a shape?
10) What is the formula for the surface area of a cone?

Total:

Quiz 2

Date: ...... / ...... / ......

1) How do you find the surface area of a prism or pyramid?
2) What is the formula for the area of a parallelogram?
3) A chord splits a circle into two parts. What is the smaller part called?
4) What is the formula $2\pi r$ for?
5) Which type of 3D shape has 1 vertex and 1 edge?
6) What is the first step in finding a ratio of volumes?
7) What do you use the formula $4\pi r^2$ to find?
8) Does a triangular prism or square-based pyramid have more vertices?
9) What is the formula for the volume of a cylinder?
10) Is the vertical height of a cone used to find its volume or its surface area?

Total:

Mixed Practice Quizzes

Quiz 3

Date: ...... / ...... / ......

1) What is the formula for the volume of a sphere?
2) What is surface area?
3) Two radii split a circle into two uneven pieces. What is the bigger piece called?
4) What is the formula for the area of a trapezium?
5) What is the volume of a cuboid with length 2 cm, width 3 cm and height 4 cm?
6) How many more faces than edges does a cylinder have?
7) What is the formula for the volume of a prism?
8) How do you use a net to find the surface area of a 3D shape?
9) What is a frustum?
10) What do you use the formula πr^2 to find?

Total:

Quiz 4

Date: ...... / ...... / ......

1) What does a rate of flow tell you?
2) What do you use the formula $2\pi rh + 2\pi r^2$ to find?
3) How do you work out the area of a composite shape?
4) What is the volume of a pyramid with base area 6 cm^2 and height 4 cm?
5) How many vertices, edges and faces does a cube have?
6) What is the formula for the volume of a cone?
7) What are the three types of projection?
8) What is the formula for the area of a sector of angle x?
9) What is a net of a shape?
10) Which type of 3D shape has 1 face and no vertices or edges?

Total:

Angles

First Go: ..... /..... /.....

Types of Angle

ACUTE angles — less than ____°

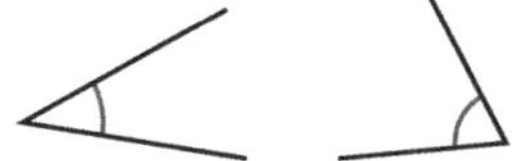

RIGHT angles — exactly ____°

OBTUSE angles — between ____° and ____°

REFLEX angles — more than ____°

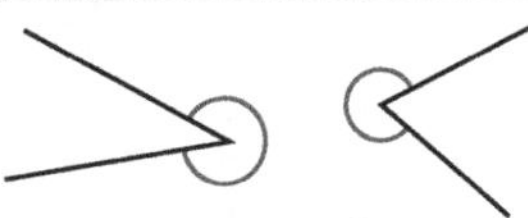

Angles can be identified using ____ letters — the ____ letter is where the angle is.

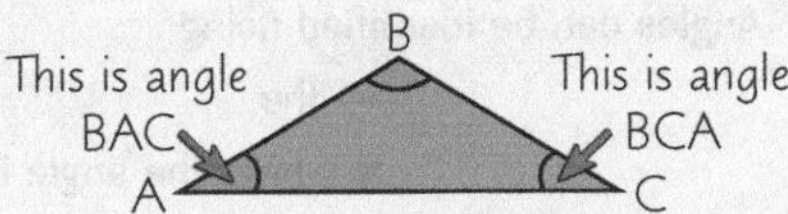

Three Steps to Measure Angles

1. **Position the ____ with its ____ along one of the angle lines.**
2. **Count up in ____ from the ____ to the other line of the angle.**
3. **Read off the angle using the ____ (the one with ____ on the start line).**

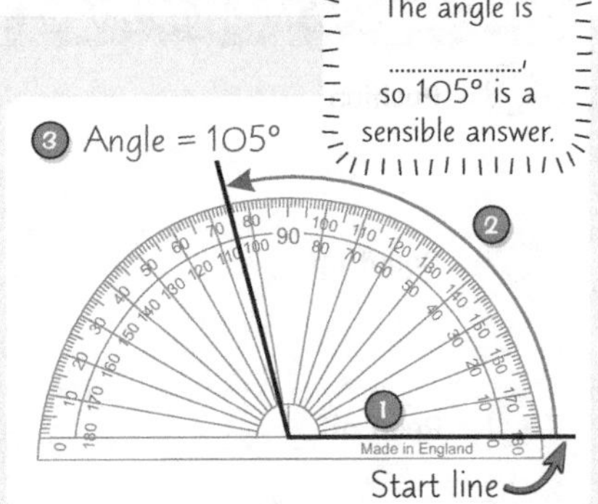

Five Angle Rules

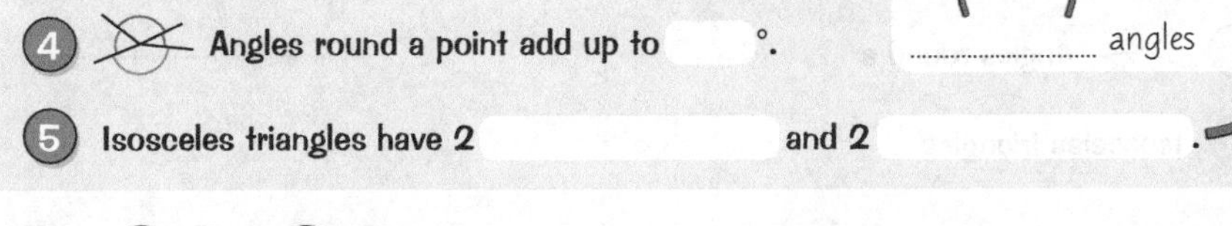

1. **Angles in a triangle add up to ____°.**
2. **Angles on a ____ add up to 180°.**
3. **Angles in a ____ add up to 360°.**
4. **Angles round a point add up to ____°.**
5. **Isosceles triangles have 2 ____ and 2 ____.**

Second Go:
...../...../.....

Angles

Types of Angle

angles — less than 90°

angles — exactly 90°

angles — between 90° and 180°

angles — more than 180°

Angles can be identified using

— the

is where the angle is.

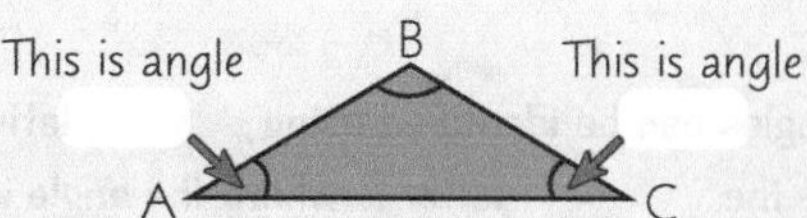

Three Steps to Measure Angles

1 Position

2 Count up

3 Read off

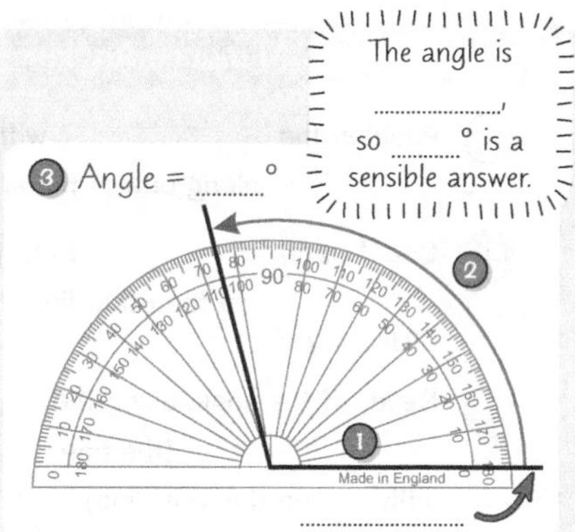

The angle is
.....................,
so .... ° is a
sensible answer.
3 Angle = ... °
2
1
Made in England
....

Five Angle Rules

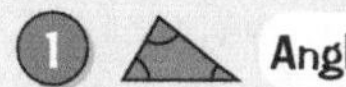 1 Angles in a .

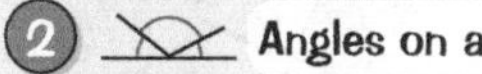 2 Angles on a .

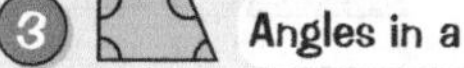 3 Angles in a .

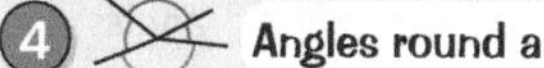 4 Angles round a .

5 Isosceles triangles .

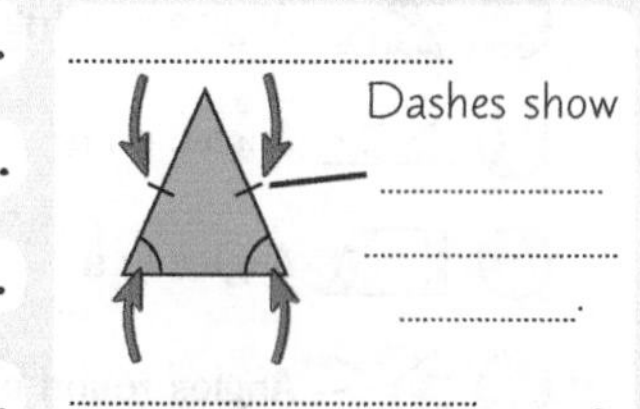

More Angles

First Go:
..... /..... /.....

Parallel and Perpendicular Lines

PARALLEL LINES — lines that are always the apart and .

PERPENDICULAR LINES — lines that meet at a .

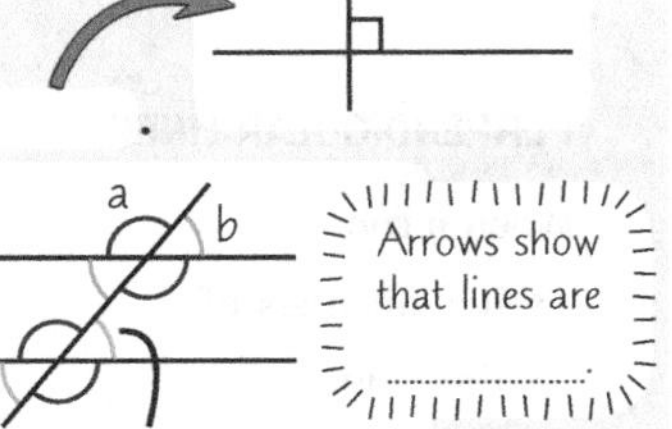

When a line crosses two :
- Two bunches of are formed.
- There are only different angles (a and b).
- angles are equal.

Alternate Angles

Found in a -shape:

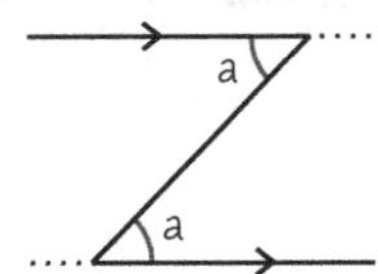

Alternate angles are the .

Corresponding Angles

Found in an -shape:

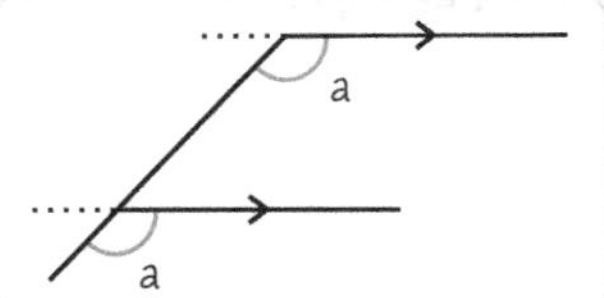

Corresponding angles are the .

Allied Angles

Found in a - or -shape:

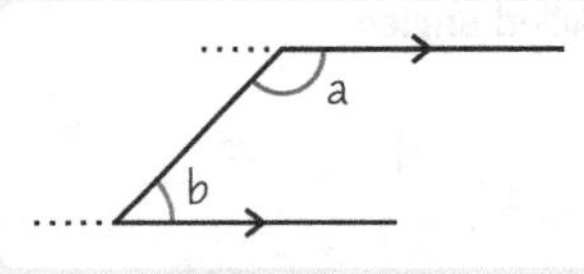

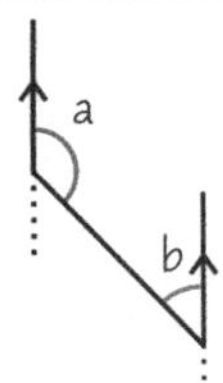

Allied angles add up to °.

$a + b =$ .... °

Interior and Exterior Angles of Polygons

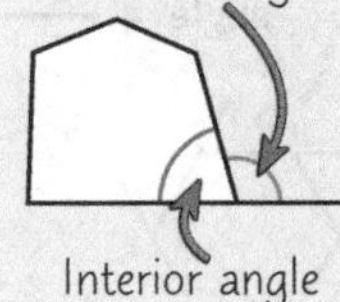

Sum of interior angles
= ( ) ×

n = number of ....

Sum of exterior angles
=

Interior angle = – exterior angle

For regular polygons only:

Exterior angle = ———

Second Go: ..... /..... /.....

More Angles

Parallel and Perpendicular Lines

PARALLEL LINES —

PERPENDICULAR LINES — .

When a line :

- Two bunches of
- There are
-

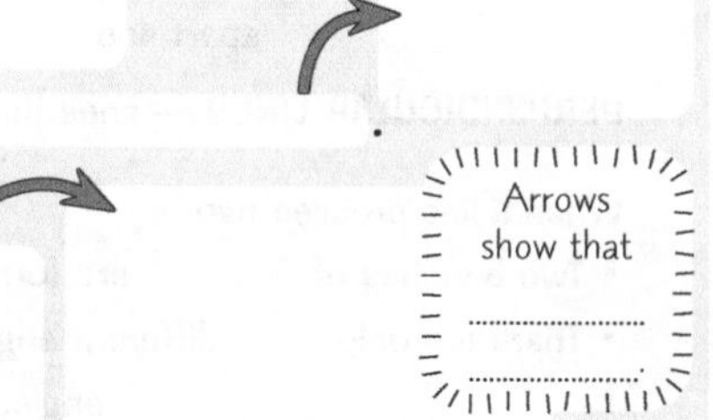

Arrows show that ....

Alternate Angles

Found in a Z-shape:

Alternate angles .

Corresponding Angles

Found in an F-shape:

Corresponding angles .

Allied Angles

Found in a C- or U-shape:

Allied angles .

...... + ... = ...°

Interior and Exterior Angles of Polygons

angle

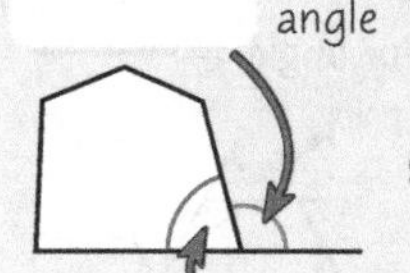

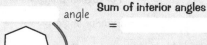

angle

Sum of interior angles =

Sum of exterior angles =

Interior angle =

n = ...

For polygons only:

angle = ———

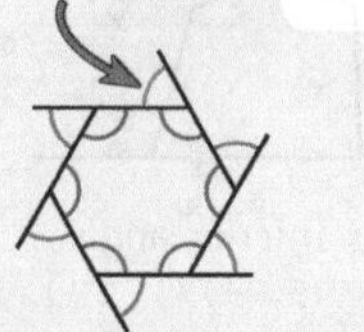

Construction

First Go:
..... /..... /.....

Triangles — Three Known Sides

1. Roughly and label the triangle.
2. Accurately draw and label the .
3. Set to each side length, then draw an at each end.
4. the ends of the with the point where the cross. points and sides.

EXAMPLE

Construct triangle ABC where AB = 3 cm, BC = 2 cm, AC = 2.5 cm.

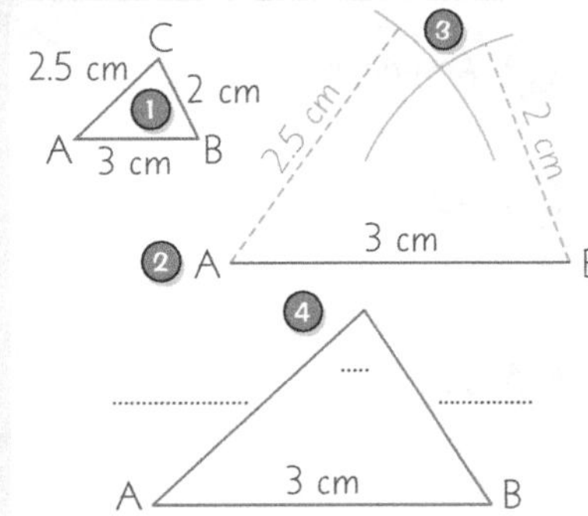

Triangles — Known Sides and Angles

1. Roughly and label the triangle.
2. Accurately draw and the base line.
3. Use a to measure the angles and mark out with .
4. If you're given two angles, draw lines from the .... of the .... through the dots. Label the intersection.

   If you're given two sides, ... the dot and label the point.
5. the points. Label known sides and angles.

EXAMPLE

Construct triangle XYZ where XY = 2 cm, angle YXZ = 70°, angle XYZ = 40°.

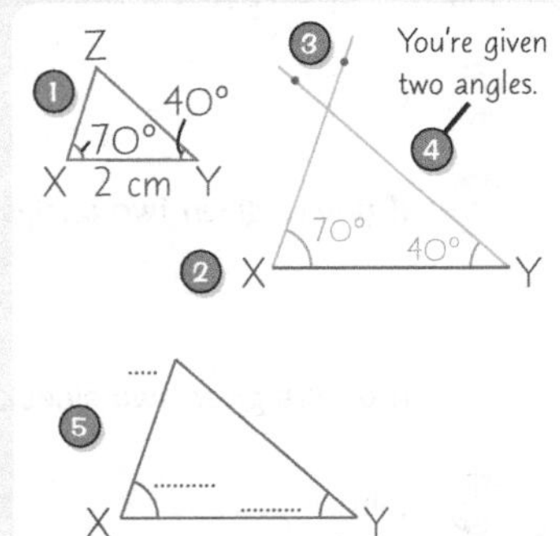

Drawing Perpendicular Lines

You'll be given a line and a point.

Keep compass settings for both arcs in each step.

Always leave your compass marks .... — don't rub them out.

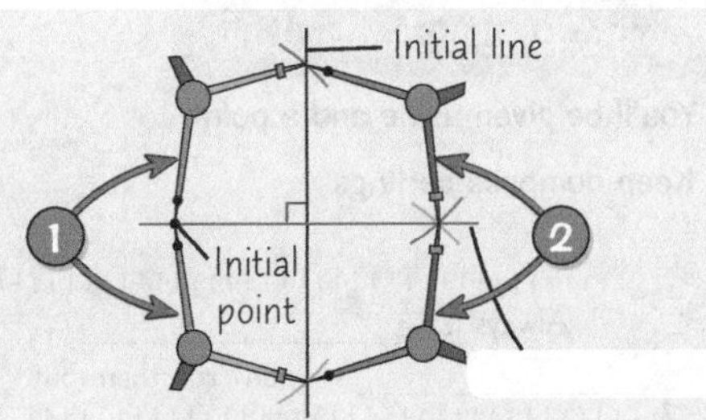

Second Go:
...../...../.....

Construction

Triangles — Three Known Sides

1. Roughly sketch and label the triangle.
2. Accurately
3. Set
4. Join

EXAMPLE

Construct triangle ABC where AB = 3 cm, BC = 2 cm, AC = 2.5 cm.

1

3

2 A 3 cm B

4

A 3 cm B

Triangles — Known Sides and Angles

1. Roughly sketch and label the triangle.
2. Accurately
3. Use
4. If you're given two angles,

   If you're given two sides,
5. Join

EXAMPLE

Construct triangle XYZ where XY = 2 cm, angle YXZ = 70°, angle XYZ = 40°.

1

3 4 You're given two angles.

2 X 2 cm Y

5

X 2 cm Y

Drawing Perpendicular Lines

You'll be given a line and a point.

Keep compass settings

Always leave .... — don't rub them out.

Construct the perpendicular from the initial point to the initial line to the right.

Initial line

Initial point

Construction and Loci

First Go: ..... /..... /.....

Constructing 60° Angles

Keep compass settings for 60° angles.

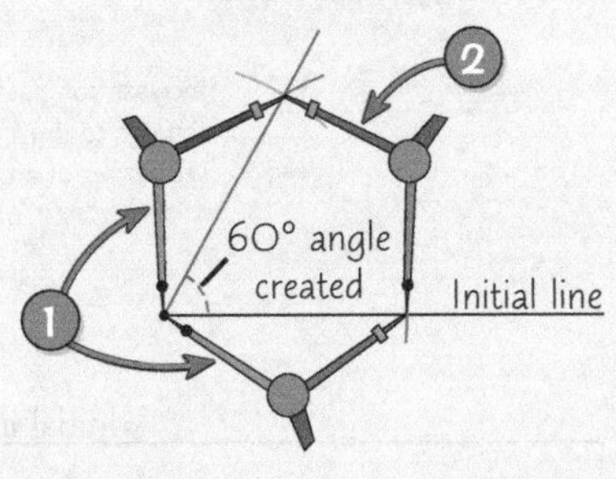

Constructing 90° Angles

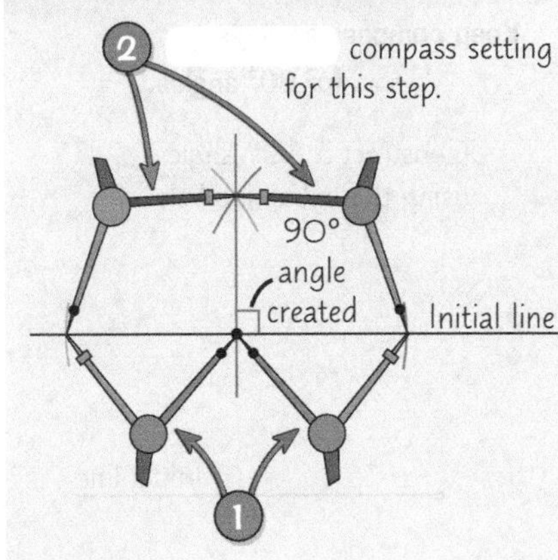

Four Different Types of Loci

LOCI — lines or regions showing that fit a given rule.

1. **Locus of points from a given point:**

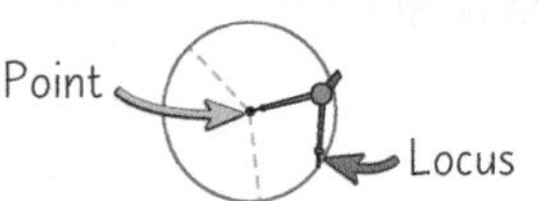

2. **Locus of points from a given line:**

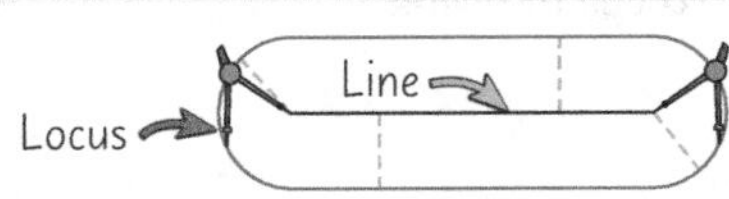

3. **Locus of points from two given lines:**

This locus .... the angle between the two lines.

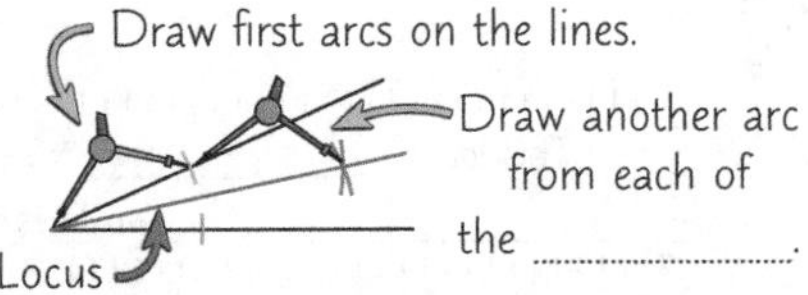

4. **Locus of points from two given points:**

When constructing any of these four loci, keep your compass settings ....

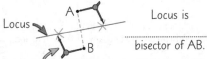

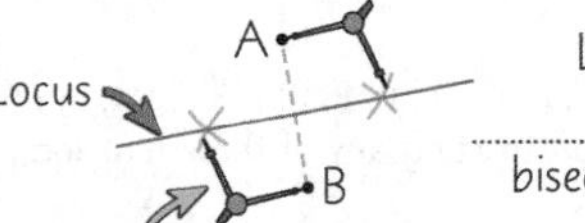

Second Go:
...../...../.....

Construction and Loci

Constructing 60° Angles

Keep compass settings

for 60° angles.

Construct a 60° angle using the initial line below.

Initial line

Constructing 90° Angles

Construct a 90° angle using the initial line below.

Increase compass settings to draw the second set of arcs.

Initial line

Four Different Types of Loci

LOCI — .

1. **Locus of points**

Point

Locus

2. **Locus of points**

Line

Locus

3. **Locus of points**

This locus .... the two lines.

Draw first arcs ....

Draw another arc from ....

....

Locus

4. **Locus of points**

When constructing any of these four loci, ...

A

Locus

B

Locus is ....

Use compasses to draw arcs from ....

Mixed Practice Quizzes

Angling for a better grade? Try these quizzes — they test everything on p.107-114. Mark them yourself when you've finished, then put your feet up and reflex.

Quiz 1

Date: ...... / ...... / ......

1) What are acute angles?
2) What is the first thing you should do when constructing a triangle?
3) What shape is the locus of points at a fixed distance from a given point?
4) What are perpendicular lines?
5) True or false? Angles on a straight line add up to 360°.
6) Explain how you draw a perpendicular line from a point to a line.
7) What is the formula for the sum of the interior angles of a polygon?
8) What piece of equipment do you use to measure angles?
9) Angles a and b are corresponding. Angle a = 104°. What is the size of angle b?
10) When constructing 90° angles, do you increase, decrease or keep the compass settings the same to draw the second set of arcs?

Total:

Quiz 2

Date: ...... / ...... / ......

1) How many identical angles does an isosceles triangle have?
2) Explain how you construct a 60° angle, given an initial line.
3) What is a locus?
4) An angle measures 128°. What sort of angle is it?
5) What is the formula for an exterior angle of a regular polygon?
6) When constructing a triangle, what is the first bit you draw accurately?
7) There are two angles around a point. One of them measures 150°. What is the size of the other angle?
8) Which type of locus has a sausage shape?
9) True or false? Vertically opposite angles add up to 180°.
10) What does the locus of points equidistant from two lines do to the angle between them?

Total:

Mixed Practice Quizzes

Quiz 3

Date: ...... / ...... / ......

1) What shape is the locus of points at a fixed distance from a given line? ✓
2) What do the angles in a triangle add up to? ✓
3) What would you do once you've drawn the base line when constructing a triangle with two known angles? ✓
4) True or false? You need to use a pair of compasses to construct a triangle with three known sides. ✓
5) What are reflex angles? ✓
6) What is the final thing you should do when constructing a triangle? ✓
7) What type of angles are found in a Z-shape? ✓
8) What is the first thing you'd do to measure an angle? ✓
9) What do the exterior angles of a polygon add up to? ✓
10) Which type of locus is the same as the perpendicular bisector of a line AB? ✓

Total:

Quiz 4

Date: ...... / ...... / ......

1) What are parallel lines? ✓
2) True or false? You keep compass settings the same when constructing 60° angles. ✓
3) How many degrees are there in a right angle? ✓
4) How many arcs do you need to draw at each step to construct perpendicular lines given a line and a point? ✓
5) When you're constructing a triangle with three known sides, what do you do after drawing and labelling the base line? ✓
6) Angles a and b are allied. Angle a = 50°. What is the size of angle b? ✓
7) What do the angles in a quadrilateral add up to? ✓
8) Which type of locus forms a circle? ✓
9) How can you find an interior angle of a polygon if you know the exterior angle? ✓
10) How do you construct the locus of points equidistant from two lines? ✓

Total:

Bearings and Scale Drawings

First Go: ..... /..... /.....

Bearings

BEARING — a given as an . Bearings must be given as (e.g. ° not 80°).

Three steps to find bearings:

1. Put your pencil at the point you're going .
2. Draw a at that point.
3. Measure the angle from the to the line joining the two points.

EXAMPLE

Find the bearing of X from Y.

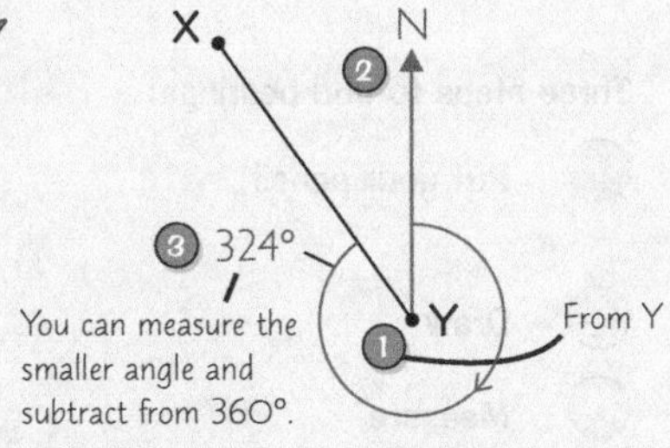

So the bearing of X from Y is °.

Map Scales

Three types of map scale:

1. 1 cm = 2 km
2. 0 km
3. 1 : 200 000

These all mean: "1 cm on the map represents in real life".

If the scale doesn't have units, use the for both sides then convert to sensible units for the context. E.g. here, 200 000 cm = m = km

To convert between maps and real life:

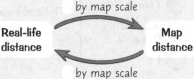

Real-life distance → by map scale → Map distance

Map distance → by map scale → Real-life distance

EXAMPLE

The scale on a map is 1:2000. How far would 2.5 cm on the map be in real life in m?

Multiply by map scale: .... × .... = ... cm

Convert cm to m: .... cm ÷ .... = ... m

Scale Drawings

EXAMPLE

0.5 cm represents 1 m

Diagram: 1.5 cm long, 0.5 cm wide

Real life: m long, m wide

Real life: 2 m long, 1 m wide

Diagram: cm long, cm wide

Second Go:
...../...../.....

Bearings and Scale Drawings

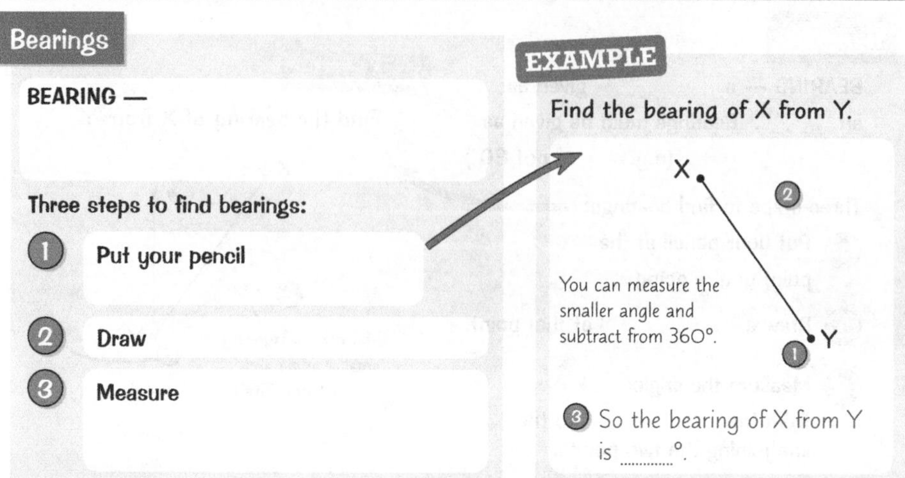

Bearings

BEARING —

Three steps to find bearings:

1. **Put your pencil**
2. **Draw**
3. **Measure**

EXAMPLE

Find the bearing of X from Y.

X
2
Y
1
You can measure the smaller angle and subtract from 360°.

3 So the bearing of X from Y is ....°.

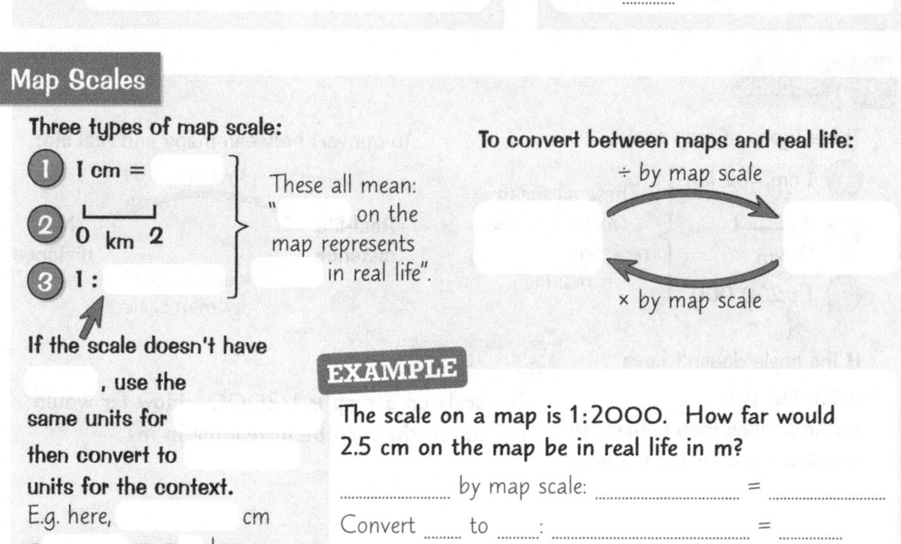

Map Scales

Three types of map scale:

1. **1 cm =**
2. **0 km 2**
3. **1 :**

These all mean: " on the map represents in real life".

If the scale doesn't have , use the same units for then convert to units for the context.

E.g. here, cm = m = km

To convert between maps and real life:

÷ by map scale

× by map scale

EXAMPLE

The scale on a map is 1:2000. How far would 2.5 cm on the map be in real life in m?

.... by map scale: .... = ...

Convert .... to ....: .... = ...

Scale Drawings

EXAMPLE

0.5 cm represents 1 m

Diagram: 1.5 cm long, 0.5 cm wide

Real life:

0.5 cm

Sofa

Real life: 2 m long, 1 m wide

Diagram:

Pythagoras' Theorem and Trigonometry

First Go: ..... /..... /.....

Pythagoras' Theorem

Uses two sides to find :

+ =

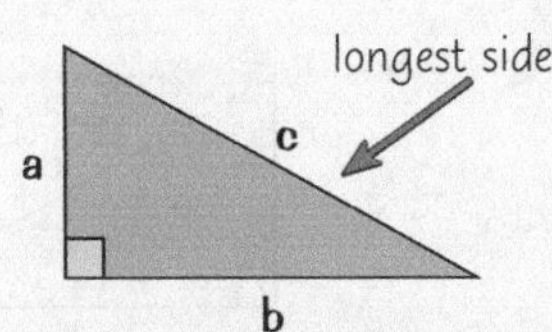

Pythagoras' theorem only works for ....

Three Steps to Use It

1. both numbers.
2. To find the longest side, ... the two squared numbers.

   To find a shorter side, ... the .... number from the .... one.
3. Take .

EXAMPLE

Find the length of AB to 1 d.p.

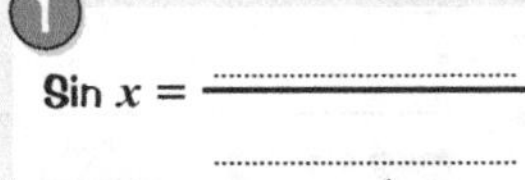

1. $9^2 =$, $4^2 =$
2. $AB^2 =$ $^2 -$ $^2 =$ $-$

   $=$

   AB is a shorter side so subtract.
3. AB = = m

   = m (1 d.p.)

Three Trigonometry Formulas

1. Sin $x =$ $\frac{\text{..........}}{\text{..........}}$

   SOH

   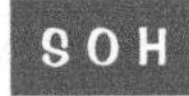
   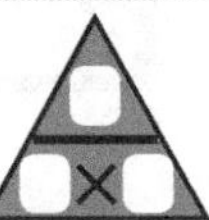
2. Cos $x =$ $\frac{\text{..........}}{\text{..........}}$

   CAH

   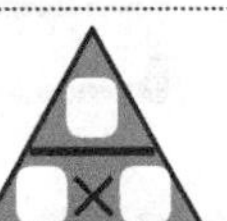
3. Tan $x =$ $\frac{\text{..........}}{\text{..........}}$

   TOA

   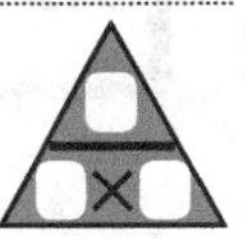

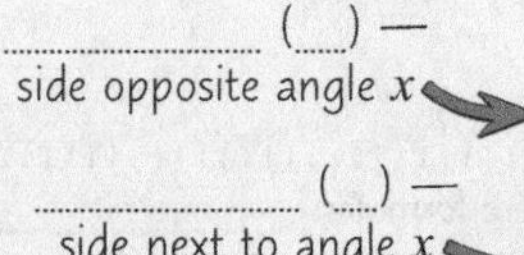

These formulas only work on ....

Remember to learn the formulas.

To use a formula triangle:

- the thing you want.
- Write down .

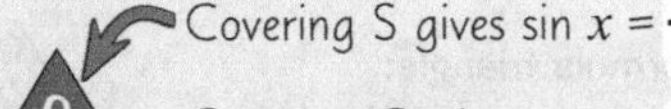

Covering S gives sin $x =$ ——

Covering O gives opp =

Covering H gives hyp = ——

Second Go:
..... /..... /.....

Pythagoras' Theorem and Trigonometry

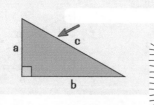

Pythagoras' Theorem

Uses
to find :

a
c
b

Pythagoras' theorem
....
....
....

Three Steps to Use It

1. Square
2. To find the longest side,

   To find a shorter side,
3. Take

EXAMPLE

Find the length of AB to 1 d.p.

A B 9 m 4 m C

1. ,
2. $AB^2 =$ =
   =
3. $AB =$
   =

Three Trigonometry Formulas

1. ....
2. ....
3. ....

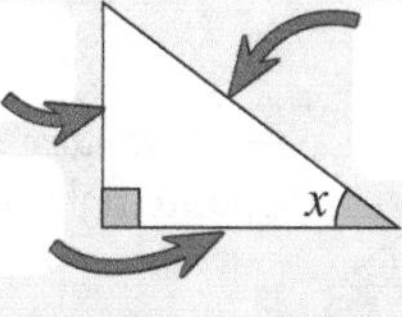

These formulas ....
....

Remember
to learn the .

To use a formula triangle:

- Cover up
- Write down

O
S × H

Covering S gives

Covering O gives

Covering H gives

Trigonometry

First Go: ..... /..... /.....

Find a Missing Length

1. Label sides .
2. Choose .
3. Use a formula triangle to .
4. Put in and work out .

EXAMPLE

Find the length of g to 2 s.f.

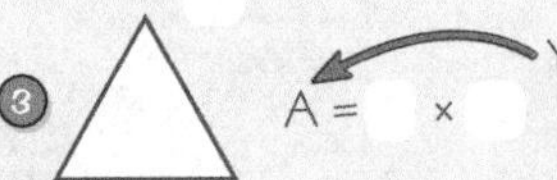

1.
2. and are involved, so use .

SOH CAH TOA

3. A = × (You're finding A.)

4. $g =$ ×
= = cm (2 s.f.)

Find a Missing Angle

1. Label sides .
2. Choose .
3. Use a formula triangle to .
4. Put in .
5. Take to find .

EXAMPLE

Find angle x to 1 d.p.

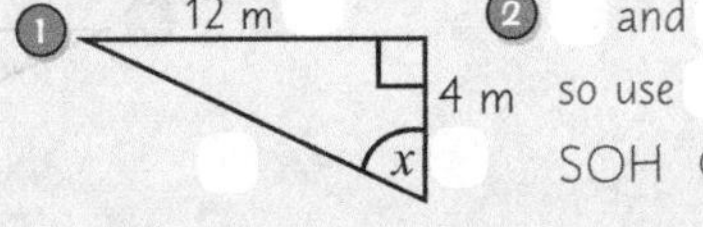

1.
2. and are involved, so use .

SOH CAH TOA

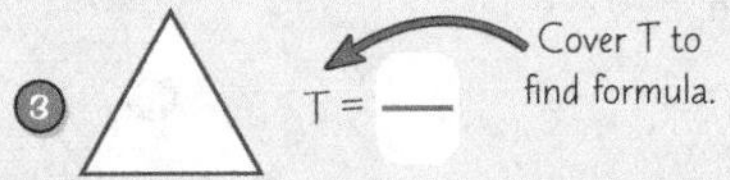

3. T = —— (Cover T to find formula.)

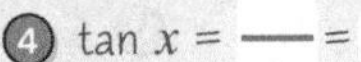

4. $\tan x =$ —— =

5. $x =$ = ° = ° (1 d.p.)

Common Trig Values

Use these common trig values to find exact values in triangles.

$\sin \quad = \frac{1}{2}$ $\sin 60° =$ $\sin \quad = \frac{1}{\sqrt{2}}$

$\cos 30° =$ $\cos \quad = \frac{1}{2}$ $\cos 45° =$

$\tan \quad = \frac{1}{\sqrt{3}}$ $\tan 60° =$ $\tan \quad = 1$

$\sin 0° =$

$\sin \quad = 1$

$\cos 0° =$

$\cos \quad = 0$

$\tan 0° =$

Second Go:
...../...../.....

Trigonometry

Find a Missing Length

1. Label
2. Choose
3. Use a
4. Put in

EXAMPLE

Find the length of g to 2 s.f.

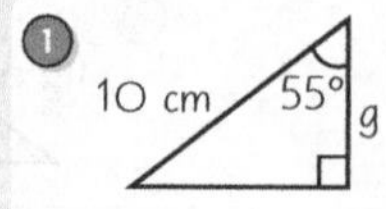

2

SOH CAH TOA

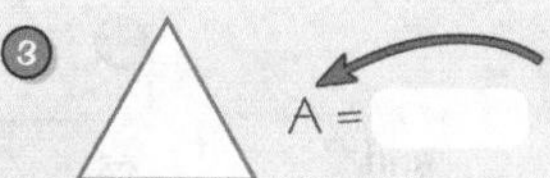

4 g =
=

Find a Missing Angle

1. Label
2. Choose
3. Use a
4. Put in
5. Take

EXAMPLE

Find angle x to 1 d.p.

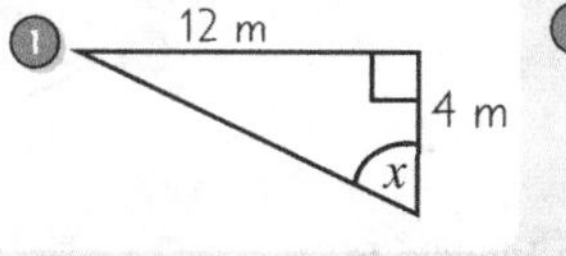

2

SOH CAH TOA

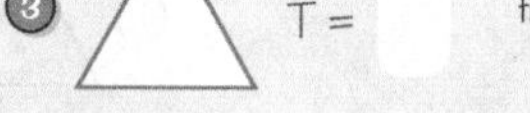

4 $\tan x =$

5 $x =$
=

Common Trig Values

Use these common trig values to find exact values in triangles.

sin = sin = sin =
cos = cos = cos =
tan = tan = tan =

sin =
sin =
cos =
cos =
tan =

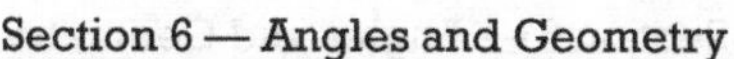

Vectors

First Go: ..... /..... /.....

Vector Notation

Vectors have both and .

Different ways of writing vectors:

- or **a** — underlined or
- — the vector from A to B.
- $\begin{pmatrix} 5 \\ -3 \end{pmatrix}$ — vector (units right, units down)

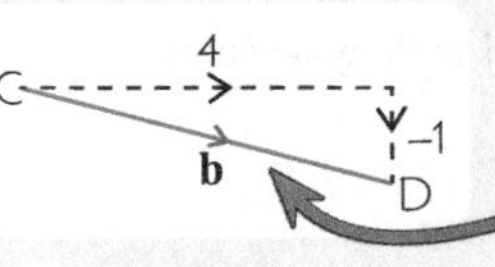

This vector can be written as: , **b**, or $\begin{pmatrix} 4 \\ -1 \end{pmatrix}$.

Multiplying a Vector by a Number

Multiplying a vector by:

+ a positive number changes its only — its stays the same.

− a negative number changes the and the direction.

Vectors that are multiples of each other are ....

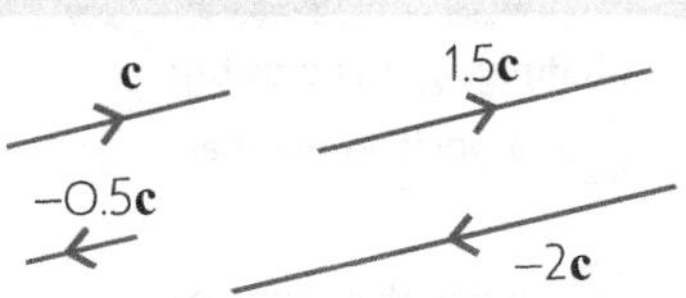

$\mathbf{a} = \begin{pmatrix} -2 \\ 3 \end{pmatrix}$ $2\mathbf{a} = 2\begin{pmatrix} -2 \\ 3 \end{pmatrix} = \begin{pmatrix} -2 \times 2 \\ 3 \times 2 \end{pmatrix} =$ ....

$-3\mathbf{a} = -3\begin{pmatrix} -2 \\ 3 \end{pmatrix} = \begin{pmatrix} -2 \times -3 \\ 3 \times -3 \end{pmatrix} =$ ....

Adding and Subtracting Vectors

a + b means "go along then along "

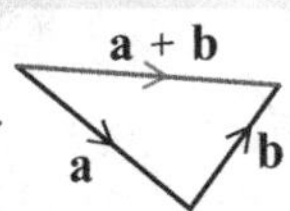

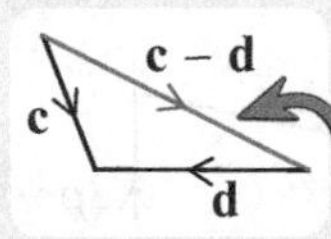

c − d means "go along then along "

To describe a movement between points:

1. Find made up of .
2. vectors along route. vectors travelled in direction.

For column vectors: add/subtract , then add/subtract .

E.g. $\begin{pmatrix} 4 \\ -1 \end{pmatrix} - \begin{pmatrix} 2 \\ 3 \end{pmatrix} = \begin{pmatrix} 4-2 \\ -1-3 \end{pmatrix} =$ ....

EXAMPLE

Find vector $\overrightarrow{AD}$ in terms of **p** and **q**.

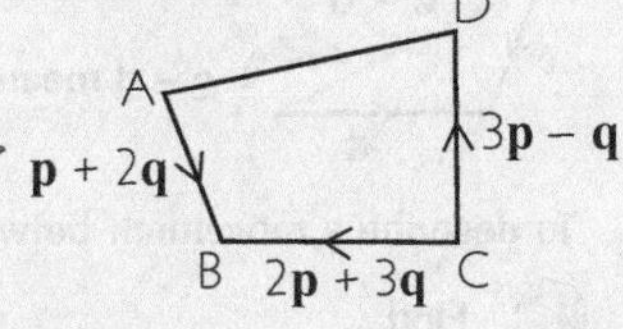

1. $\overrightarrow{AD} =$ + +
2. = ( ) − ( ) + ( ) = −

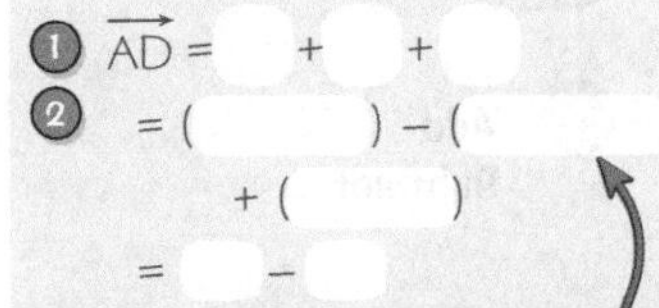

Watch out for the direction of the arrows — the vector given is actually $\overrightarrow{CB}$ so you need to subtract it to go along $\overrightarrow{BC}$.

Second Go: ...../...../.....

Vectors

Vector Notation

Vectors .

Different ways of writing vectors:

- or a — or
- $\overrightarrow{AB}$ — the vector .
- $\begin{pmatrix} 5 \\ -3 \end{pmatrix}$ — (,)

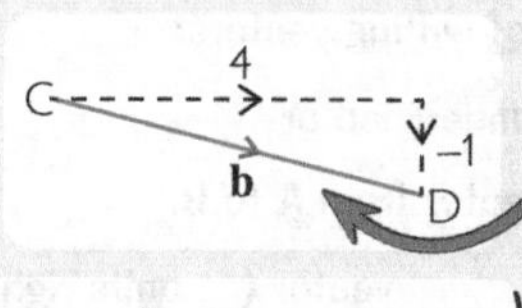

This vector can be written as: , **b**, or .

Multiplying a Vector by a Number

Multiplying a vector by:

+ a positive number

− a negative number

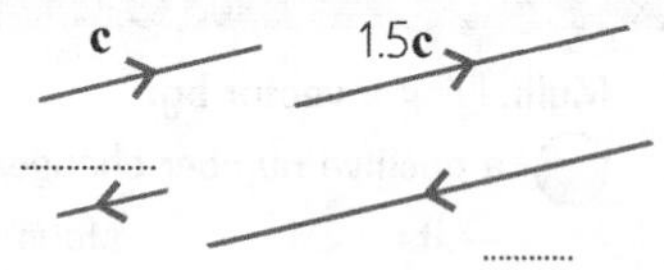

....

....

Vectors that are .... of each other are ....

$\mathbf{a} = \begin{pmatrix} -2 \\ 3 \end{pmatrix}$ $2\mathbf{a} = 2\begin{pmatrix} -2 \\ 3 \end{pmatrix} =$ .... = ...

$-3\mathbf{a} = -3\begin{pmatrix} -2 \\ 3 \end{pmatrix} =$ .... = ...

Adding and Subtracting Vectors

<u>a</u> + <u>b</u> means

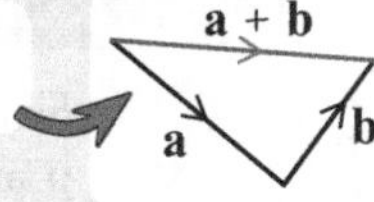

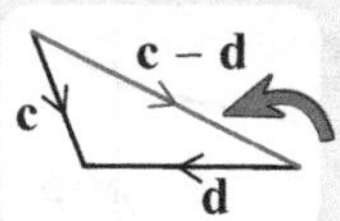

<u>c</u> − <u>d</u> means

To describe a movement between points:

1. Find
2. Add
   Subtract

For column vectors:

E.g. $\begin{pmatrix} 4 \\ -1 \end{pmatrix} - \begin{pmatrix} 2 \\ 3 \end{pmatrix} =$ .... = ...

EXAMPLE

Find vector $\overrightarrow{AD}$ in terms of **p** and **q**.

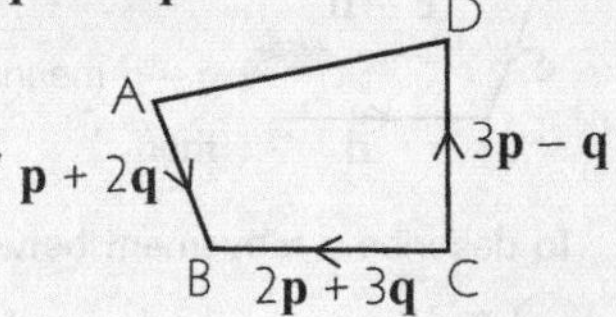

1. $\overrightarrow{AD} =$
2. =

=

Watch out for the direction of the arrows — the vector given is actually $\overrightarrow{CB}$ so you need to subtract it to go along $\overrightarrow{BC}$.

Mixed Practice Quizzes

Questions on Pythagoras are as easy as a^2 b^2 c^2 but others might be a bit triggy. Try these quizzes testing p.117-124, mark them, then add up your score.

Quiz 1

Date: ...... / ...... / ......

1) How would you write 85° as a bearing?
2) What is the name given to the longest side of a right-angled triangle?
3) True or false? SOH CAH TOA only works on right-angled triangles.
4) In a column vector, what do the top and bottom numbers show?
5) What is the first thing you need to do when using Pythagoras' theorem?
6) What is the exact value of sin 30°?
7) When using trig to find a missing side or angle, what is the first thing you should do?
8) A map has the scale 1 cm = 5 km. How far apart in real life are two towns that are 2.5 cm apart on the map?
9) Which trig formula should you use if you know the opposite and adjacent?
10) $\underline{a} = \begin{pmatrix} -1 \\ 7 \end{pmatrix}$. Give $2\underline{a}$ as a column vector.

Total:

Quiz 2

Date: ...... / ...... / ......

1) What does SOH CAH TOA stand for?
2) Where should you draw a north line when finding the bearing of A from B?
3) Are vectors that are multiples of each other parallel or perpendicular?
4) How do you convert from a map distance to a real-life distance?
5) What is the formula for Pythagoras' theorem?
6) What happens to a vector when you multiply it by a positive number?
7) What is the exact value of cos 45°?
8) Which trig formula should you use if you know the adjacent and hypotenuse?
9) Find $\begin{pmatrix} -2 \\ 3 \end{pmatrix} + \begin{pmatrix} 4 \\ 5 \end{pmatrix}$.
10) A scale drawing has the scale 1 cm = 5 m. What are the measurements on the scale drawing of a lake that measures 25 m by 40 m in real life?

Total:

Mixed Practice Quizzes

Quiz 3

Date: ...... / ...... / ......

1) What is the formula triangle for cos x?
2) How do you convert from a real-life distance to a map distance?
3) True or false? Pythagoras' theorem only works on equilateral triangles.
4) Are bearings measured clockwise or anticlockwise from the north line?
5) Find $\begin{pmatrix} 2 \\ 5 \end{pmatrix} - \begin{pmatrix} 3 \\ -3 \end{pmatrix}$.
6) Which trig formula should you use if you know the opposite and hypotenuse?
7) Two cities are 50 km apart in real life. On a map, the distance between them is 2.5 cm. What is the map scale in the form 1 cm : n km?
8) What happens to a vector when you multiply it by a negative number?
9) When using trig to find a missing side or angle, how do you choose which trig formula to use?
10) Which trig value is equal to $\sqrt{3}$?

Total:

Quiz 4

Date: ...... / ...... / ......

1) What is the name given to the side next to the known angle in a right-angled triangle?
2) What two characteristics do vectors have?
3) What is the last thing you need to do when using Pythagoras' theorem?
4) A scale drawing has scale 1 cm = 2 m. What are the real-life dimensions of a rug that measures 2 cm by 1.5 cm on the scale drawing?
5) When using trig, what is the next thing you have to do to find an angle once you've put the numbers into the formula?
6) On a map with a scale of 1:50 000, how many m does 1 cm represent?
7) What is the formula triangle for tan x?
8) $\underline{a} = \begin{pmatrix} 6 \\ 2 \end{pmatrix}$. Give $-3\underline{a}$ as a column vector.
9) What is the value of cos 0°?
10) In triangle ABC, $\overrightarrow{AB} = \underline{a}$ and $\overrightarrow{CB} = \underline{b}$. Find $\overrightarrow{AC}$ in terms of $\underline{a}$ and $\underline{b}$.

Total:

Probability Basics

First Go: ..... /..... /.....

The Probability Scale

All probabilities are between ..... and .....

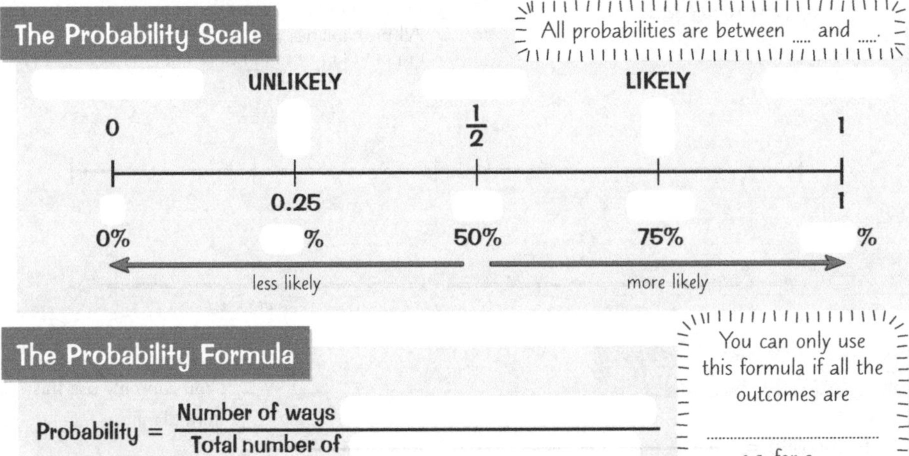

The Probability Formula

$$\text{Probability} = \frac{\text{Number of ways}}{\text{Total number of}}$$

You can only use this formula if all the outcomes are .... — e.g. for a .... coin, dice or spinner.

EXAMPLE

What is the probability of picking a prime number at random from a bag of counters numbered 1-15?

The prime numbers between 1 and 15 are 2, 3 5, 7, 11 and 13 — 6 in total.

$$\text{Probability} = \frac{\text{number of ways of ....}}{\text{total number of ....}} = \frac{.....}{.....} = \frac{.....}{.....}$$

There are 15 counters so 15 possible outcomes.

Probabilities of Events

If only one possible outcome can happen at a time, the of all possible outcomes add up to . As events either happen or :

P( ) + P(event doesn't happen) =

So:

P(event doesn't happen) = – P( )

EXAMPLE

The probability of getting a 5 on a spinner is 0.65. What is the probability of not getting a 5?

P(not 5) = – P(5)
= – 0.65
=

Sample Space Diagrams

These show .

Can be a simple or a .

You can use them to find .

×	1	2	3
2	2		6
4		8	
6	6		

P(event) means "the .... of the .... happening".

E.g. All possible outcomes when two fair spinners numbered 1, 2, 3 and 2, 4, 6 are spun and the results .

There are 9 possible outcomes and 2 of them are 6, so P(6) = —.

Second Go:
...../...../.....

Probability Basics

The Probability Scale

All probabilities are ....

less likely — more likely

The Probability Formula

Probability = ――――――――――

You can only use this formula if .... — e.g. for a ....

EXAMPLE

What is the probability of picking a prime number at random from a bag of counters numbered 1-15?

Probability = $\frac{\dots\dots}{\dots\dots} = \frac{\dots}{\dots} = \frac{\dots}{\dots}$

Probabilities of Events

If only one possible outcome can happen at a time, the probabilities of all possible outcomes .

As events either or :

So:

EXAMPLE

The probability of getting a 5 on a spinner is 0.65. What is the probability of not getting a 5?

P(not 5) =

=

=

P(event) means ".."

Sample Space Diagrams

These show

Can be

You can use them to

×			

E.g. All possible outcomes when two fair spinners numbered 1, 2, 3 and 2, 4, 6 are spun and the results multiplied.

There are possible outcomes and of them are 6, so P(6) = .

Probability Experiments

First Go: ..... /..... /.....

Repeating Experiments

FAIR — every outcome is to happen.

BIASED — some outcomes are than others.

Relative frequency = $\frac{}{\text{Number of times}}$

Use relative frequencies to probabilities.

The more times you do an experiment, the more the estimate is likely to be.

EXAMPLE

A spinner labelled A to D is spun 100 times. It lands on C 48 times. Find the relative frequency of spinning a C and say whether you think this spinner is biased.

Relative frequency of C = $\frac{48}{100}$ = ...

If the spinner was fair, you'd expect the relative frequency of C to be ..... ÷ ..... = ...

.... is much larger than ...., so the spinner is probably ....

Frequency Trees

Used to record results when experiments have . For example:

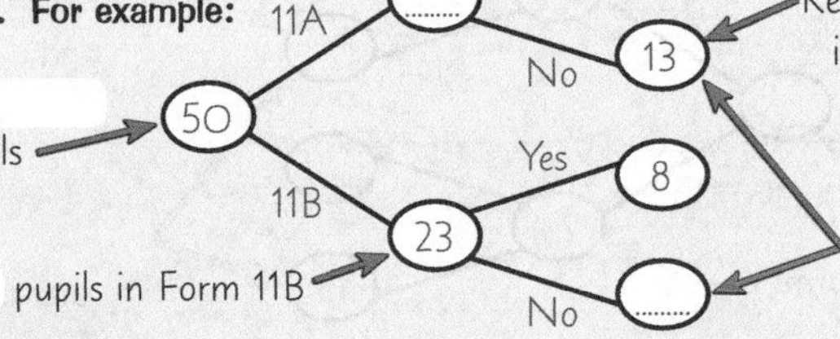

of pupils

pupils in Form 11B

pupils from 11A are in the choir

Relative frequency of pupils in 11A and not in choir = =

+ = pupils aren't in the choir

Expected Frequency

EXPECTED FREQUENCY — how many times you'd something to happen in a certain .

Expected frequency = ×

Use the .... from previous experiments if you don't know the probability.

EXAMPLE

A fair 6-sided dice is rolled 360 times. How many times would you expect it to land on 4?

P(4) =

Expected frequency of 4 = × =

Second Go:
..... /..... /.....

Probability Experiments

Repeating Experiments

FAIR —

BIASED —

Relative frequency =

Use relative frequencies to . **The**
you do an experiment, the **is likely to be.**

EXAMPLE

A spinner labelled A to D is spun 100 times. It lands on C 48 times. Find the relative frequency of spinning a C and say whether you think this spinner is biased.

Relative frequency of C = $\frac{\dots}{\dots}$ = ...

If the spinner was ...., you'd expect the relative frequency of C to be ....
.... is much .... than ...., so the spinner is probably ....

Frequency Trees

Used to
when experiments have
. 11A
For example:

Choir?
Form
Yes
14
No
Yes
No
11B
27
23
15
14 pupils from
Relative frequency of pupils in
and
= =
pupils
aren't in the choir
pupils in Form

Expected Frequency

EXPECTED FREQUENCY —

Expected frequency
=

Use the .... from ....
.... if you don't know the ....

EXAMPLE

A fair 6-sided dice is rolled 360 times. How many times would you expect it to land on 4?

P(4) =

Expected frequency of 4

= =

The AND/OR Rule and Tree Diagrams

First Go: ..... /..... /.....

The AND Rule

INDEPENDENT EVENTS — where one event happening the of another event happening.

For independent events A and B:

P(A and B) = ×

This rule only works for .... events.

EXAMPLE

A fair dice is rolled and a fair coin is tossed. What is the probability of rolling a 2 and getting heads?

P(2) = and P(heads) =

Rolling a dice and tossing a coin are independent, so:

P(2 and heads) = × =

The OR Rule

Use the OR rule when events at the same time.

For events A and B:

P(A or B) = +

EXAMPLE

A bag contains 12 balls numbered 1–12. What is the probability of selecting either an even number or a 5?

P(even) = and P(5) =

So P(even or 5) = + =

Tree Diagrams

Used to work out probabilities for — e.g. for a bag containing 3 red and 2 blue counters that are selected at random and without replacement:

Probabilities on each set of branches that meet at a point .

First counter

Second counter

along the branches to get the end probabilities.

$\frac{3}{5}$ R: $\frac{2}{4}$ R — $\frac{3}{5} \times \frac{2}{4} =$

B — $\frac{3}{5} \times \quad =$

B: $\frac{3}{4}$ R — $\times \frac{3}{4} =$

B — $\times \quad =$

The end probabilities add up to 1:

+ + +

= = 1

The second selection is by the results of the first — so the probabilities are .

If the counters were replaced, the probabilities on each set of branches would be ....

Pick the right end probability to answer questions:

E.g. $P(B, B) = \frac{2}{20} =$

Second Go: ..... /..... /.....

The AND/OR Rule and Tree Diagrams

The AND Rule

INDEPENDENT EVENTS —

For independent events A and B:

P(A and B) =

This rule only works ....

EXAMPLE

A fair dice is rolled and a fair coin is tossed. What is the probability of rolling a 2 and getting heads?

P( ) = and P( ) =

Rolling a dice and tossing a coin are , so:

P( ) = =

The OR Rule

Use the OR rule when .

For events A and B:

P(A or B) =

EXAMPLE

A bag contains 12 balls numbered 1–12. What is the probability of selecting either an even number or a 5?

P( ) = and P( ) =

So P( ) = =

Tree Diagrams

Used to work out — e.g. for a bag containing 3 red and 2 blue counters that are selected at random without replacement:

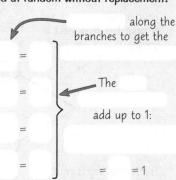

on each set of branches that meet at a point .

First counter

Second counter

$\frac{3}{5}$

R, B (first counter); R, B, R, B (second counter)

along the branches to get the .

=

=

=

=

The add up to 1:

= = 1

The selection is affected by the — so the probabilities are .

If the counters were ...., the .... on each set of branches would be ....

Pick the right to answer questions:

E.g. P(B, B) = =

Sets and Venn Diagrams

First Go: ..... /..... /.....

Set Notation

SET — a collection of (e.g. numbers), written in .

Sets can be written in different ways:

- list of — e.g. A = {1, 4, 9, 16}
- — e.g. A = {square numbers less than 20}
- — e.g. A = {x : x is a square number less than 20}

ξ	the (the group of things elements are selected from).
	the number of elements in set A.

Sets and Venn Diagrams

VENN DIAGRAM — a diagram where are represented by .

The rectangle represents the .

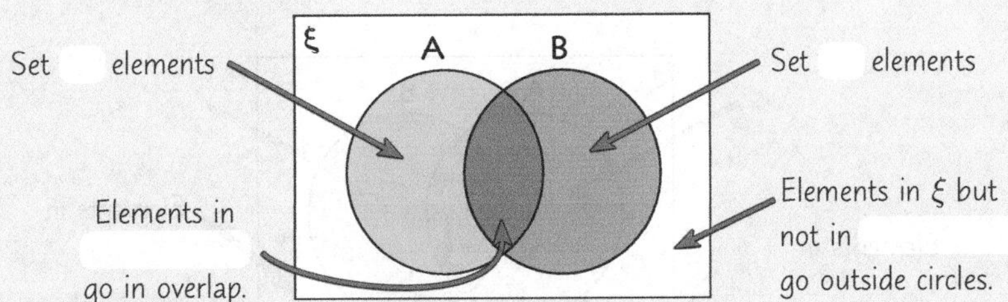

Probabilities from Venn Diagrams

Venn diagrams can show either the .... or the elements themselves.

EXAMPLE

There are 150 pupils in Year 11. 75 of them have a cat, 92 of them have a dog and 22 of them have a cat and a dog. Draw a Venn diagram to show this information, and use it to find the probability that a randomly selected pupil will have a cat or a dog, but not both.

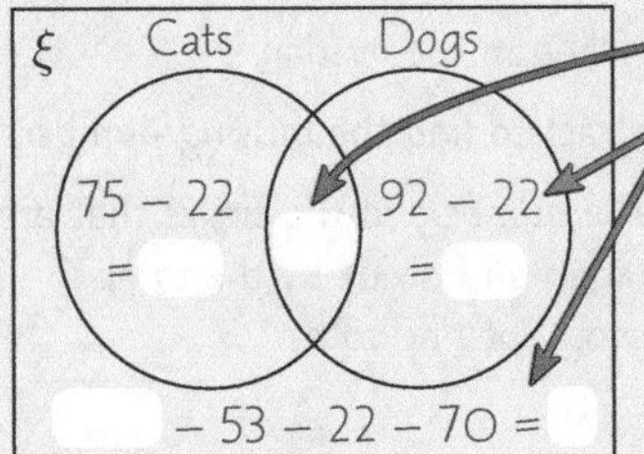

Start by filling in the overlap.

Then subtract to find the missing numbers.

Add up the numbers in the circles that aren't in the overlap and divide by the total:

P(cat or dog but not both)

Second Go:
...../...../.....

Sets and Venn Diagrams

Set Notation

SET —

Sets can be written in different ways:

- — e.g. A = {1, 4, 9, 16}
- **description** — e.g. A = { }
- **formal notation** — e.g. A = { }

ξ	
n(A)	

Sets and Venn Diagrams

VENN DIAGRAM —

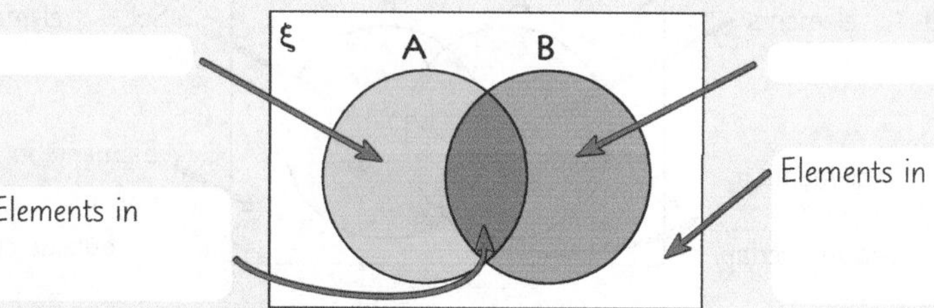

Probabilities from Venn Diagrams

Venn diagrams can show either the .... or the ....

EXAMPLE

There are 150 pupils in Year 11. 75 of them have a cat, 92 of them have a dog and 22 of them have a cat and a dog. Draw a Venn diagram to show this information, and use it to find the probability that a randomly selected pupil will have a cat or a dog, but not both.

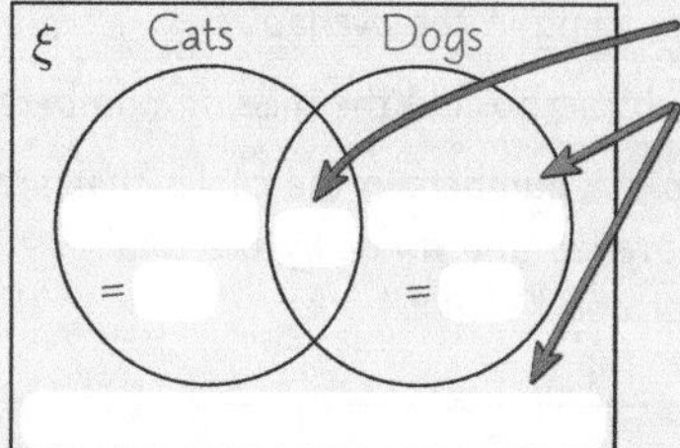

Start by filling in the overlap.

Then subtract to find the missing numbers.

Add up the numbers in the circles that aren't in the overlap and divide by the total:
P(cat or dog but not both)

= = =

Mixed Practice Quizzes

Expected number of quizzes testing p.127-134 = 4, and I haven't disappointed. Have a go at the questions AND mark your answers... OR you'll be missing out.

Quiz 1

Date: ...... / ...... / ......

1) How likely is an event with a probability of 0?
2) What is the formula for relative frequency?
3) How do you find the end probabilities on a tree diagram?
4) True or false? If two cards are picked at random from a pack without replacement, the probabilities are different for the second pick.
5) A bag contains counters numbered 1 to 20. One counter is selected at random. What is the probability of selecting a multiple of 5?
6) What does the symbol ξ represent?
7) What is expected frequency?
8) What is the AND rule for independent events A and B?
9) The relative frequency of a five-sided spinner landing on side 1 is 0.5. Do you think the spinner is fair or biased?
10) On a Venn diagram, which area contains elements in both sets A and B?

Total:

Quiz 2

Date: ...... / ...... / ......

1) If you know P(event happens), how do you find P(event doesn't happen)?
2) What does it mean if a dice or spinner is fair?
3) What does the rectangle on a Venn diagram represent?
4) True or false? An event with a probability of 0.75 is likely to happen.
5) What are frequency trees used for?
6) What does it mean if two events are independent?
7) On a Venn diagram, where do elements that are only in set A go?
8) What is a sample space diagram?
9) On a tree diagram, three branches meet at a point. Two of the branches each have probability 0.3. What is the probability on the third branch?
10) What is a set?

Total:

Mixed Practice Quizzes

Quiz 3

Date: ...... / ...... / ......

1) What is the probability of rolling a 2 on a fair six-sided dice?
2) What number goes at the start of a frequency tree?
3) A fair spinner numbered 1, 2, 3 is spun twice and the scores are added up. Describe a sample space diagram you could draw for this experiment.
4) For the set A = {2, 3, 5, 7}, what is n(A)?
5) How do you get more accurate estimates of probabilities from experiments?
6) How likely is an event with a probability of 1?
7) What does the overlap between the circles on a Venn diagram represent?
8) What do the probabilities on a set of branches that meet at a point on a tree diagram add up to?
9) The probability of getting a 1 on a spinner is 0.25. How many times would you expect to get a 1 if you spun the spinner 60 times?
10) Events A and B can't both happen at the same time. P(A) = 0.35 and P(B) = 0.1. Find P(A or B).

Total:

Quiz 4

Date: ...... / ...... / ......

1) A dice is rolled one hundred times and lands on 4 twenty times. What is the relative frequency of rolling a 4?
2) What do the end probabilities on a tree diagram add up to?
3) A Venn diagram with sets A and B represents 50 people. 35 people belong to set A or B (or both). What number goes outside the circles?
4) Give the formula for the probability if all possible outcomes are equally likely.
5) What does it mean if a dice or spinner is biased?
6) What is the OR rule for events A and B that can't happen at the same time?
7) A bag contains different coloured counters. The probability of picking a red counter is 0.45. What is the probability of picking a counter that isn't red?
8) What is the formula for expected frequency?
9) Find P(A and B) for independent events where P(A) = 0.4 and P(B) = 0.2.
10) On a Venn diagram, where do elements of ξ that aren't in set A or B go?

Total:

Sampling and Data Collection

First Go: ..... /..... /.....

Definitions of Sampling Terms

POPULATION	The you want to find out about.
	A smaller group taken from the population.
RANDOM SAMPLE	A sample in which every member of the population has an of being included.
REPRESENTATIVE	the whole population.
	Doesn't fairly represent the whole population.
	Data described by words (not numbers).
QUANTITATIVE DATA	Data described by .
DISCRETE DATA	Data that can only take .
	Data that can take any value in a range.

Choosing a Simple Random Sample

1. Give each member of the population a .
2. Make a list of .
3. the members of the with those numbers.

Random numbers can be chosen using a ...., or from a ....

Spotting Bias

Two things to think about:

1. , and the sample is taken.
2. How the sample is.

- If any groups have been , it won't be random.
- If it isn't big enough, it won't be .
- Bigger samples should be more .

Questionnaires

Questions should be:

- and easy to
  e.g. specifies a time period
- Easy to answer
- (not leading or biased)

How long do you spend exercising each week?

☐ < 1 hour
☐ ≥ 1 and < 3 hours
☐ ≥ 3 and < 5 hours
☐ ≥ 5 hours

Response boxes should:

- Cover all options
  e.g. 'more than' and 'less than' options
- Not
  e.g. 1 hour can only go in one box
- Not be in different ways

Second Go:
...../...../.....

Sampling and Data Collection

Definitions of Sampling Terms

	The whole group you want to find out about.
SAMPLE	
RANDOM SAMPLE	
	Fairly represents the whole population.
	Doesn't fairly represent the whole population.
QUALITATIVE DATA	
QUANTITATIVE DATA	
	Data that can only take exact values.
	Data that can take any value in a range.

Choosing a Simple Random Sample

1. Give
2. Make
3. Pick

Random numbers can be chosen using a

....

Spotting Bias

Two things to think about:

1. When
2. How

- If any groups
- If it isn't
- Bigger

Questionnaires

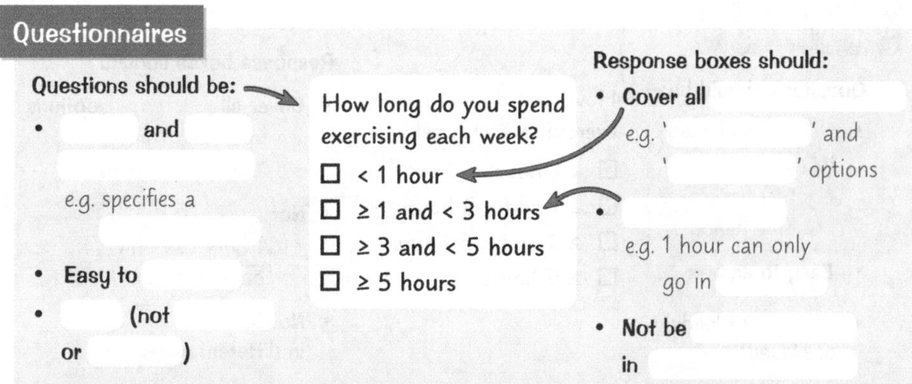

Questions should be:
• and
e.g. specifies a
• Easy to
• (not
or)
How long do you spend exercising each week?
☐ < 1 hour
☐ ≥ 1 and < 3 hours
☐ ≥ 3 and < 5 hours
☐ ≥ 5 hours
Response boxes should:
• Cover all
e.g. ' ' and
' ' options
•
e.g. 1 hour can only go in
• Not be
in

Simple Charts and Graphs

First Go: ..... /..... /.....

Pictograms

PICTOGRAM — uses to show .

E.g. number of cars in a car park

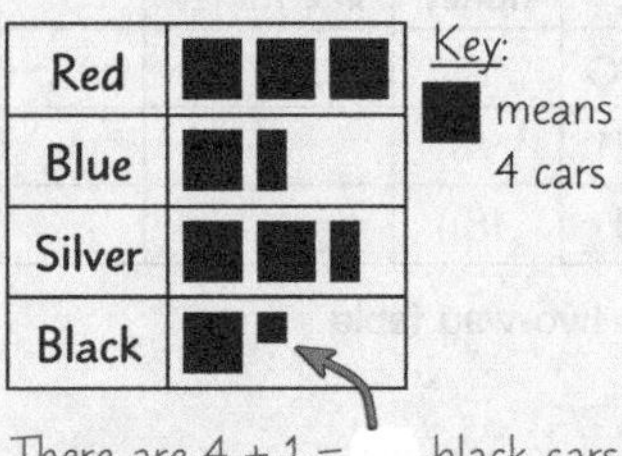

There are 4 + 1 = black cars

Two-Way Tables

TWO-WAY TABLE — shows there are in each category.

	Likes honey	Doesn't like honey	Total
Year 10	85		158
Year 11	96	82	178
Total		155	336

To fill in a two-way table, / using the information you're given to find .

Bar Charts

BAR CHART — height of bar shows .

Compare data sets using ... ...or .

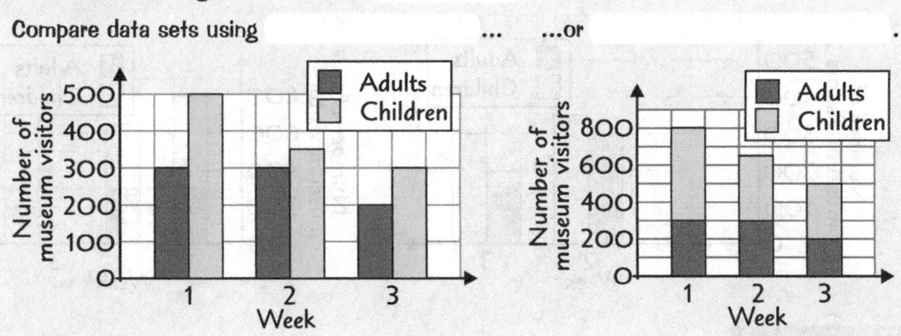

Time Series

TIME SERIES — a line graph showing the same thing measured at .

A time series shows if there is (a basic repeating pattern).

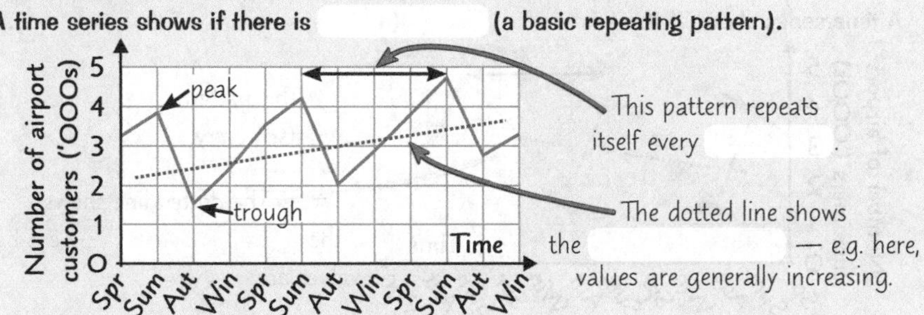

Second Go: ...../...../.....

Simple Charts and Graphs

Pictograms

PICTOGRAM —

E.g. number of cars in a car park

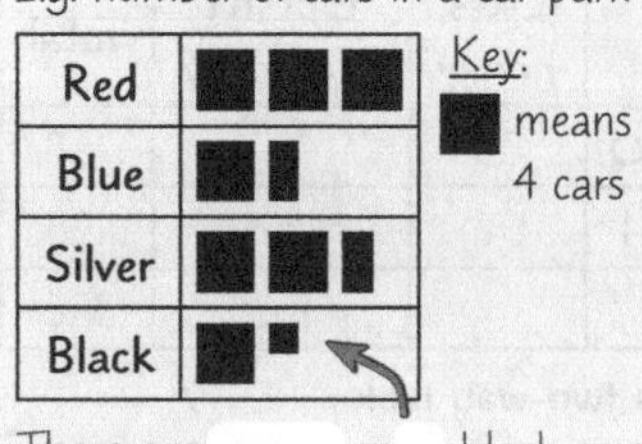

There are = black cars

Two-Way Tables

TWO-WAY TABLE —

	Likes honey	Doesn't like honey	Total
Year 10		73	
Year 11	96		178
Total	181		

To fill in a two-way table

Bar Charts

BAR CHART —

using ... ...or

Complete the missing bars in each chart using the data in the other chart.

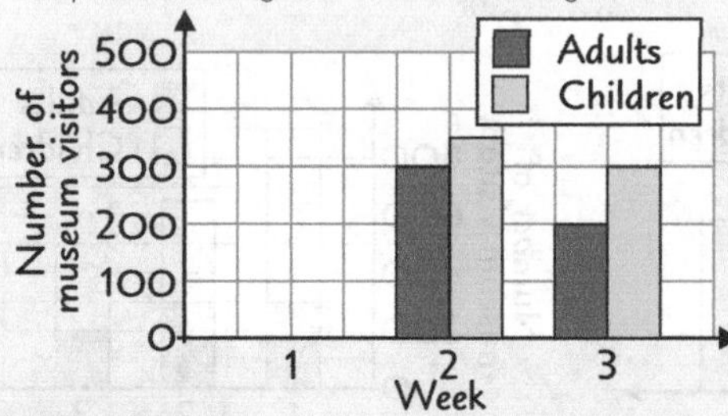

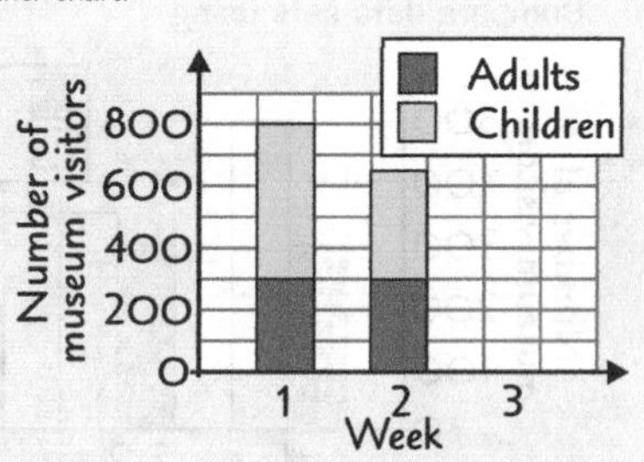

Time Series

TIME SERIES —

A time series shows if there is (a).

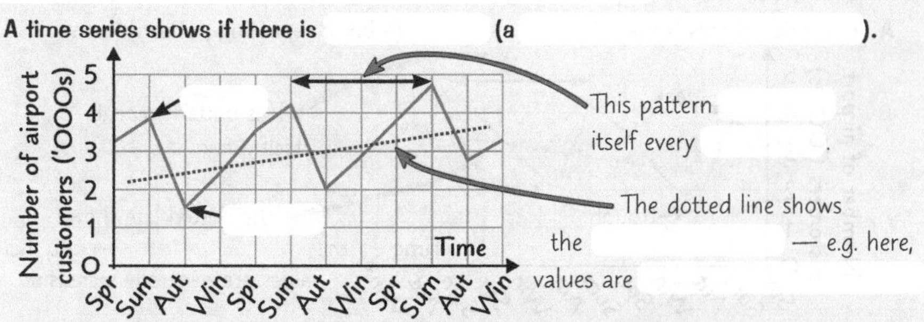

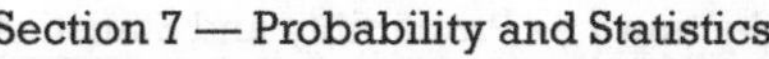

Pie Charts

First Go: ..... /..... /.....

Pie Charts and Proportion

Total of all data = °

Work out missing and of the total using the information given.

This pie chart shows how some pupils travel to school.

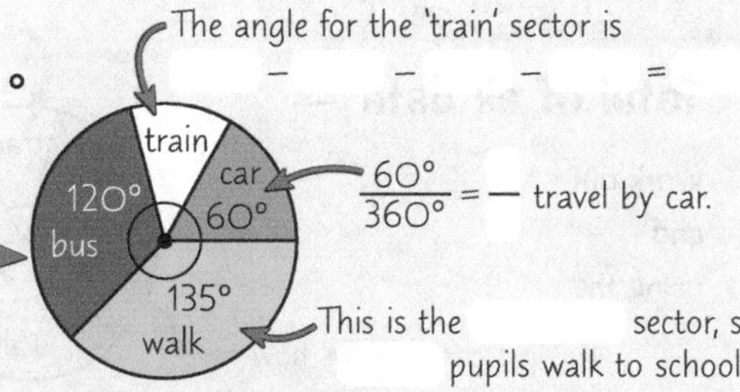

Four Steps to Draw Pie Charts

1. the numbers to find the .
2. Divide 360° by the to find the .
3. Multiply each number by the to find the .
4. Draw the pie chart using a .

EXAMPLE

1. Total = + + =
2. Multiplier = 360° ÷ = °

Club	Drama	Art	Band
Number	15	8	17
Angle		72°	153°

3. E.g. 15 × ° = °

Check that the angles add up to 360°:
° + 72° + 153°
= °

4.

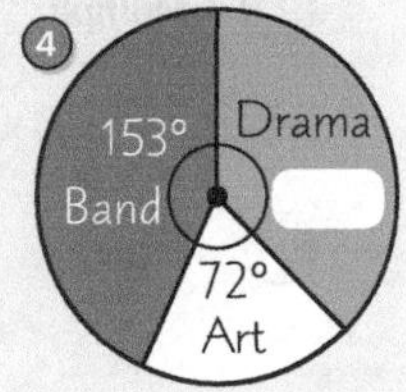

Two Steps to Find How Many in a Category

1. Divide 360° by the to find the angle for .
2. Divide the angle for a by the angle for .

EXAMPLE

120 pupils were asked where they went on holiday last summer. The results are shown in the pie chart. How many pupils went to Italy?

Italy 60°, Spain 120°, France 150°, USA 30°

1. 360° ÷ .... = ...° per pupil
2. ....° ÷ ....° = ... pupils went to Italy

Second Go:
...../...../.....

Pie Charts

Pie Charts and Proportion

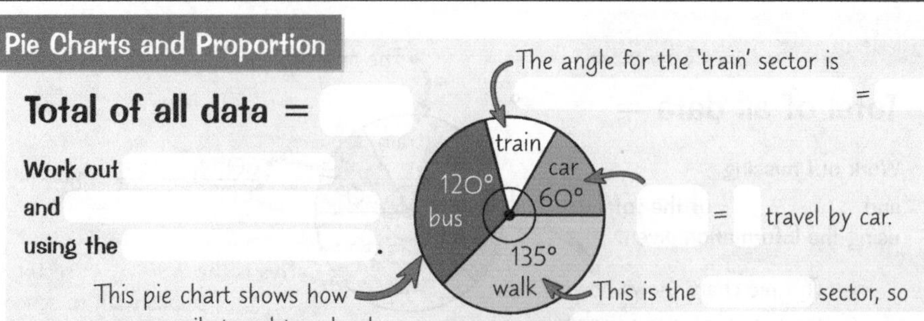

The angle for the 'train' sector is

= travel by car.

This is the sector, so

Four Steps to Draw Pie Charts

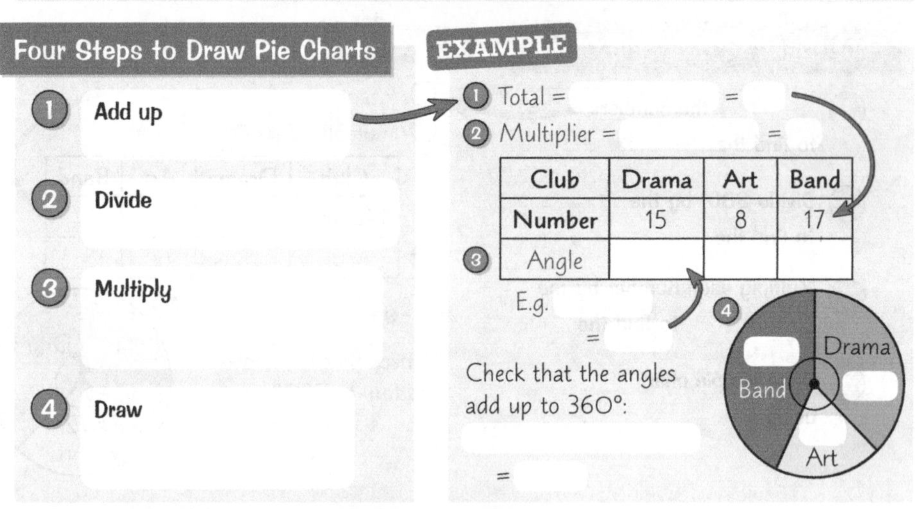

1 Add up
2 Divide
3 Multiply
4 Draw
EXAMPLE
1 Total = =
2 Multiplier = =
Club | Drama | Art | Band
Number | 15 | 8 | 17
3 Angle
E.g.
=
4
Drama
Band
Art
Check that the angles add up to 360°:
=

Two Steps to Find How Many in a Category

1 Divide .

2 Divide .

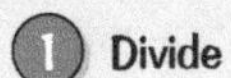

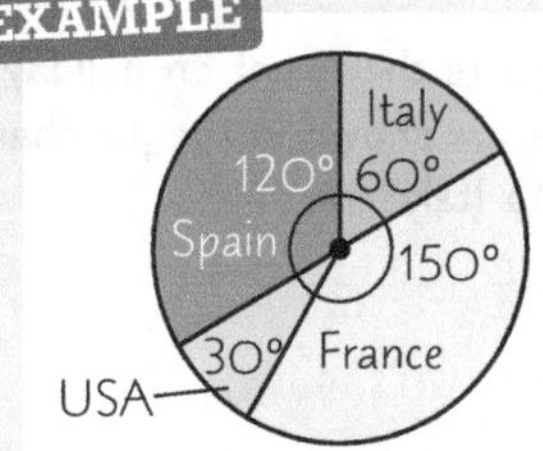

120 pupils were asked where they went on holiday last summer. The results are shown in the pie chart. How many pupils went to Italy?

1 .... = ... per pupil

2 .... = ... pupils went to Italy

Scatter Graphs

First Go: ..... / ..... / .....

Scatter Graphs and Correlation

SCATTER GRAPH — plots ________ against ________.

CORRELATION — shows how ________ the two things are ________.

Even if two things are correlated, it doesn't mean that one .... the other.

STRONG correlation	Two things are ________. Points make a ________.
	Two things are loosely related. Points don't line up quite as neatly.
	Two things are unrelated. Points are scattered randomly.
POSITIVE correlation	Two things increase or decrease ________. Points slope ________ from left to right.
	One thing increases as the other decreases. Points slope ________ from left to right.

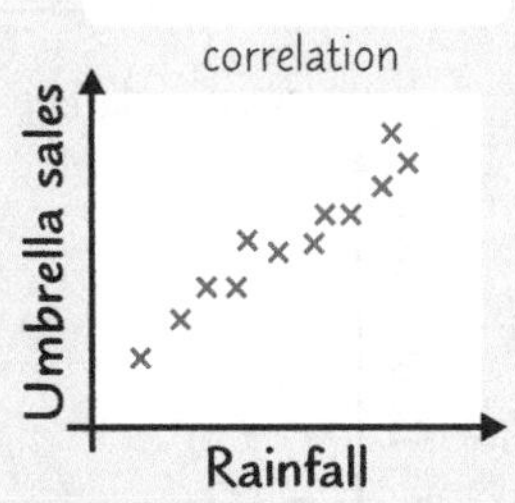

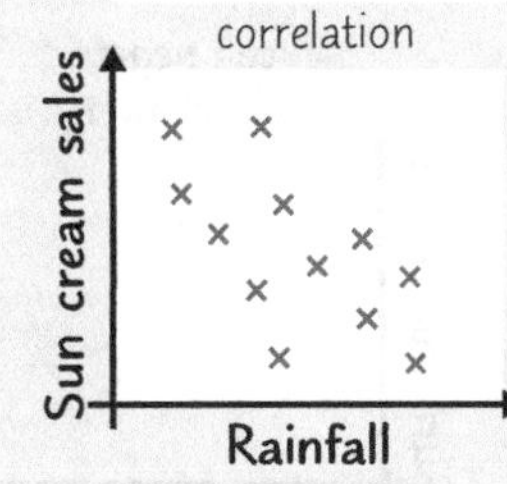

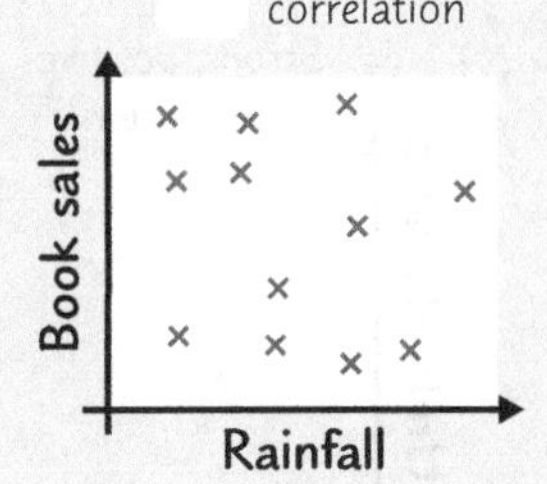

Lines of Best Fit

LINE OF BEST FIT — goes ________ or ________ most points. Shows ________ and can be used to make ________.

OUTLIER — a point that ________ the general pattern. ________ it when drawing the line of best fit.

INTERPOLATION — predicting ________ the range of data. Usually ________. Here, you'd expect a 2-year-old car to be worth about £5000.

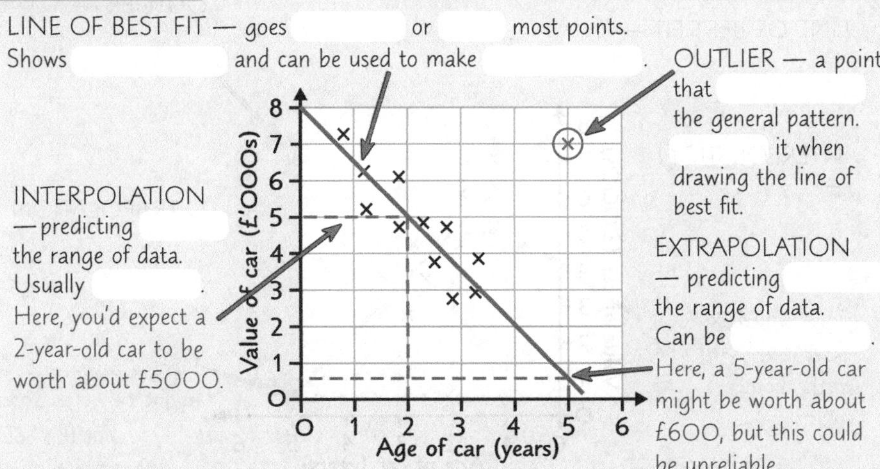

EXTRAPOLATION — predicting ________ the range of data. Can be ________. Here, a 5-year-old car might be worth about £600, but this could be unreliable.

Second Go:
...../...../.....

Scatter Graphs

Scatter Graphs and Correlation

SCATTER GRAPH —

CORRELATION —

STRONG correlation	
WEAK correlation	
NO correlation	
POSITIVE correlation	
NEGATIVE correlation	

Even if two things are ...., it doesn't mean that one .... the other.

Strong positive correlation

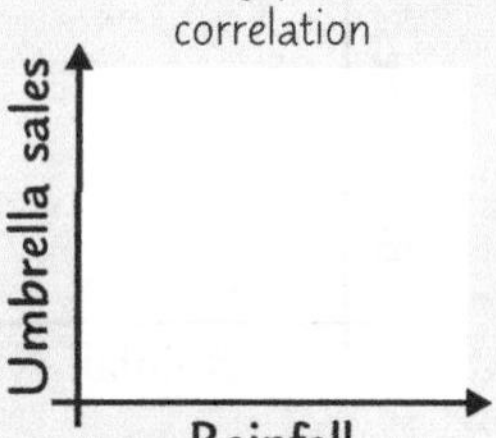

Umbrella sales / Rainfall

Weak negative correlation

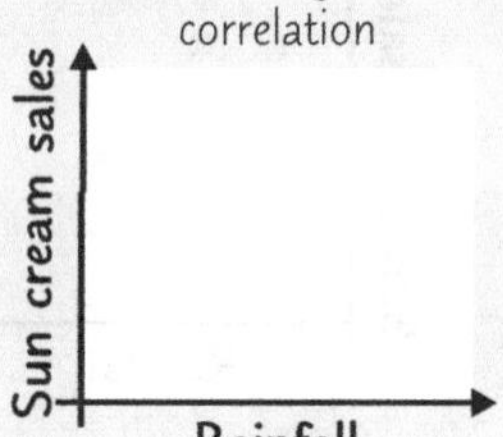

Sun cream sales / Rainfall

No correlation

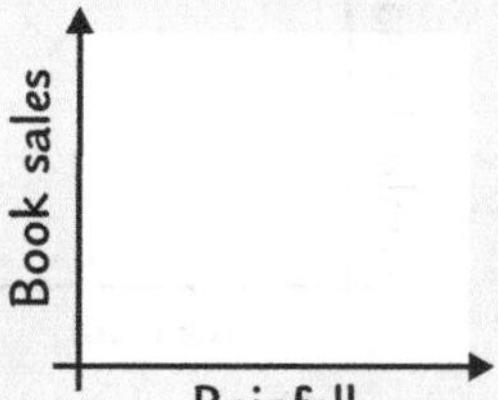

Book sales / Rainfall

Lines of Best Fit

LINE OF BEST FIT —

OUTLIER —

INTERPOLATION —

EXTRAPOLATION —

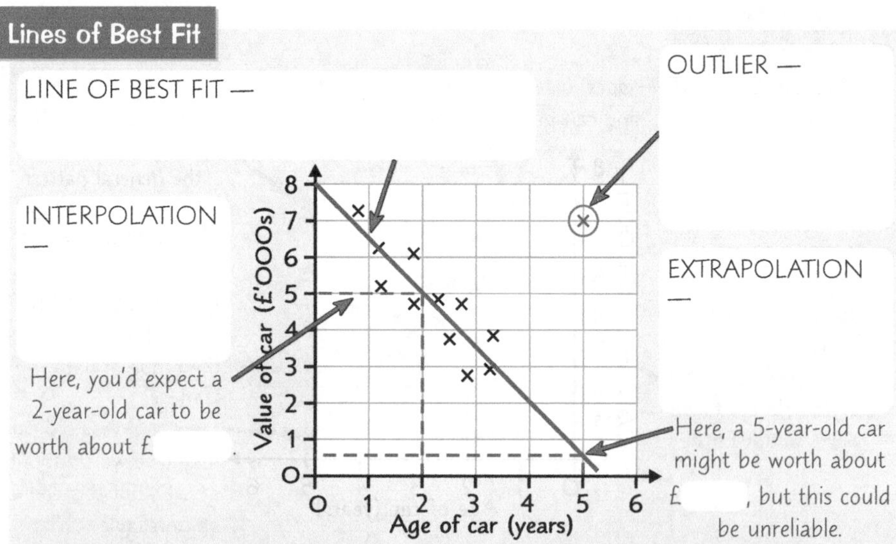

Here, you'd expect a 2-year-old car to be worth about £

Here, a 5-year-old car might be worth about £ , but this could be unreliable.

Mean, Median, Mode and Range

First Go: ...../...../.....

Mean, Median, Mode and Range

MEAN	÷
	Middle value (when values are in size order)
MODE	
	Difference between highest and lowest values

Arrange the data in order of size to find the .... It helps when finding the .... and .... too.

To find the position of the median, use the formula: (...... + ...) ÷ ......
(where ...... is the number of items)

EXAMPLE

The data below shows the ages of people in a judo club. Find the mean, median, mode and range for the data.

24 28 17 34 36 24 19 26

The mean, median and mode are all ....

Mean = + + + + + + + = = years

In order:

Position of median = (+) ÷ = th value.

So median is halfway between and , which is years.

Mode = years Range = − = years

If a data set has an ...., it can have a big effect on the .... and ...., making them misleading.

If a 62-year-old joined the judo club, this person would be an . It would make the mean 30 and the range 45, which the rest of the data well.

Comparing Data Sets

Look at the .... and .... for each data set, identify which is higher or lower and say what they mean in the .... of the data.

EXAMPLE

Some statistics for the members of a karate club are shown on the right. Compare the distribution of the ages of the karate club and the judo club.

Mean: 22 years
Median: 23 years
Range: 10 years

The mean and median values for the karate club are than the values for the judo club, so the members of the karate club are generally .

The range for the karate club is than the range for the judo club, so there is in ages for the karate club — members' ages are more .

Second Go: ..... /..... /.....

Mean, Median, Mode and Range

Mean, Median, Mode and Range

MEAN	
MEDIAN	
MODE	
RANGE	

Arrange the data in .... to find the .... It helps when finding the .... and .... too.

To find the position of the median, use the formula: ....

(where .... is the ....)

EXAMPLE

The data below shows the ages of people in a judo club. Find the mean, median, mode and range for the data.

24 28 17 34 36 24 19 26

The ...., ... and .... are all averages.

Mean = ―――――――――― = ――― =

In order:

Position of median = =

So median is between and , which is .

Mode = Range = =

If a data set has an ...., it can have a .... on the ...., making them ....

If a 62-year-old joined the judo club, this person would be an . It would make the 30 and the 45, which .

Comparing Data Sets

Look at the .... for each data set, identify which is .... and say what they mean in the ....

EXAMPLE

Some statistics for the members of a karate club are shown on the right. Compare the distribution of the ages of the karate club and the judo club.

Mean: 22 years
Median: 23 years
Range: 10 years

The mean and median values for the karate club

The range for the karate club

Finding Averages

First Go: ..... /..... /.....

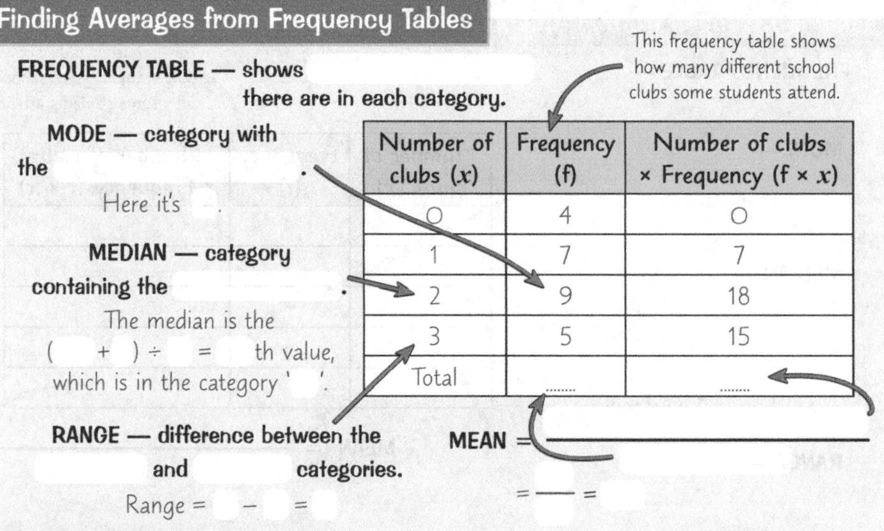

Finding Averages from Frequency Tables

FREQUENCY TABLE — shows there are in each category.

This frequency table shows how many different school clubs some students attend.

MODE — category with the .

Here it's .

MEDIAN — category containing the .

The median is the (+) ÷ = th value, which is in the category ' '.

Number of clubs (x)	Frequency (f)	Number of clubs × Frequency (f × x)
0	4	0
1	7	7
2	9	18
3	5	15
Total	....	....

RANGE — difference between the and categories.

Range = − =

MEAN = ———

= —— =

Grouped Frequency Tables

Data is grouped into classes, with no gaps between classes for data.

are used to cover all possible values.

Height (h cm)	Frequency (f)	Mid-interval value (x)	f × x
0 < h ≤ 20	12	10	120
20 < h ≤ 30	28	....	700
30 < h ≤ 40	10	35	....
Total	....	—	....

Find the mid-interval value by adding up the and dividing by . E.g. (0 + 20) ÷ 2 = .

MODAL CLASS — class with . Here it's .

CLASS CONTAINING THE MEDIAN — contains the of data.

The median is the (+) ÷ = th value. Both the th and th data values are in the class, so the class containing the median is .

RANGE — difference between the and .

Estimated range = − = cm

MEAN — multiply the (x) by the (f). Divide the total of by the .

Estimated mean = ——— = cm

You don't know the .... for grouped data so can only .... the mean and range.

Second Go:
..... /..... /.....

Finding Averages

Finding Averages from Frequency Tables

FREQUENCY TABLE —

This frequency table shows how many different school clubs some students attend.

MODE —

Here it's .

MEDIAN —

The median is the = , which is in the category ' '.

Number of clubs (x)	Frequency (f)	Number of clubs × Frequency (f × x)
0	4	....
1	7	....
2	9	....
3	5	....
Total	....	....

RANGE —

Range = =

MEAN =

= =

Grouped Frequency Tables

Data is grouped into classes, with between classes for .

Inequality symbols are used to

Height (h cm)	Frequency (f)	Mid-interval value (x)	f × x
0 < h ≤ 20	12	....	....
20 < h ≤ 30	28	....	....
30 < h ≤ 40	10	....	....
Total	....	—	....

Find the mid-interval value by

E.g. (+) ÷ = 10.

MODAL CLASS — . Here it's .

CLASS CONTAINING THE MEDIAN — .

The median is the = . Both the and data values are in the class, so the class containing the median is .

RANGE —

Estimated range = = cm

MEAN —

Estimated mean = = cm

You don't know the .... for .... so can only .... the .... and ....

Mixed Practice Quizzes

Hooray — you've made it to the last set of quizzes. Sample these questions covering everything on p.137-148, and see how many marks you can tally up.

Quiz 1

Date: ...... / ...... / ......

1) Explain how you would choose a simple random sample.
2) What is the first thing you should do when drawing a pie chart?
3) On a pictogram, what does the key tell you?
4) What is qualitative data?
5) How do you find the median of a data set?
6) What is a line of best fit?
7) What is the mid-interval value for the class $20 < x \leq 40$?
8) Name two types of bar chart that can be used to compare data sets.
9) What does strong positive correlation on a scatter graph look like?
10) How do you find the mean from a frequency table?

Total:

Quiz 2

Date: ...... / ...... / ......

1) On a bar chart, what does the height of the bars show?
2) What is discrete data?
3) What does weak negative correlation on a scatter graph look like?
4) Give one way in which a sample could be biased.
5) How do you find the range of a set of values?
6) What would be on each axis of a time series graph showing weekly sales?
7) A pie chart shows 45 items.
   How many degrees is each item represented by?
8) To estimate the mean from a grouped frequency table, what is the next thing you have to do once you've found the mid-interval values?
9) What is a population?
10) What is it called when you make predictions within the range of your data?

Total:

Mixed Practice Quizzes

Quiz 3

Date: ...... / ...... / ......

1) What is the mode of a data set?
2) What is correlation?
3) What do all the angles in a pie chart add up to?
4) What are dual bar charts useful for?
5) What would be the first step in choosing a simple random sample of pupils from a school?
6) Which two values do you use to estimate the range from a grouped frequency table?
7) Which would you expect to be more reliable, interpolation or extrapolation?
8) How do you find missing values in a two-way table?
9) Give two features of good questionnaire questions.
10) What is quantitative data?

Total:

Quiz 4

Date: ...... / ...... / ......

1) What type of bar chart has two bars stacked on top of each other for each category?
2) When drawing a line of best fit on a scatter graph, how do you deal with outliers?
3) How do you work out the mean of a data set?
4) True or false? A person's height is a piece of continuous data.
5) What is meant by seasonality on a time series graph?
6) How do you find the median from a frequency table?
7) How do you find the multiplier when drawing a pie chart?
8) What is it called when you make predictions outside the range of your data?
9) Data set A has a smaller range than data set B. What does this tell you about the values in set A compared with set B?
10) What do two-way tables show?

Total:

Answers

Section 1 — Number

Pages 13-14

Quiz 1

Q1 True

Q2 A whole number — can be positive, negative or zero.

Q3 When a number is repeated.

Q4 False — $8.62 \times 1000 = 8620$.

Q5 $12\overline{)780}$

Q6 Left

Q7 Writing a number as its prime factors multiplied together.

Q8 True

Q9 One

Q10 List all the prime factors that are in either number, then multiply them together.

Quiz 2

Q1 Positive

Q2 Prime numbers

Q3 Two

Q4 A number that is made by multiplying a whole number by itself.

Q5 The final answer.

Q6 List all the prime factors that are in both numbers, then multiply them together.

Q7 Brackets, Other, Division, Multiplication, Addition, Subtraction

Q8 A number that can only be divided by itself and 1.

Q9 No — 30 isn't in the 12 times table.

Q10 Count the total number of digits after the decimal points in 3.8 and 2.4 and give 912 that many decimal places — $3.8 \times 2.4 = 9.12$.

Quiz 3

Q1 A number that divides into it.

Q2 Remove the decimal point and the zero after it.

Q3 Positive

Q4 The multiplication

Q5 32×7 and 32×10.

Q6 90

Q7 1, 4, 9, 16

Q8 Count the number of zeros in 300 and move the decimal point in 195 that many places bigger — $65 \times 300 = 19\ 500$.

Q9 Write the division as a fraction.

Q10 The smallest number that divides by all numbers in question.

Quiz 4

Q1 A number that is made by multiplying a whole number by itself twice.

Q2 The biggest number that divides into all numbers in question.

Q3 Multiply 23 by 2.

Q4 20

Q5 2, 3, 5, 7

Q6 Negative

Q7 The subtraction

Q8 Write 2 above the line and carry the remainder 2 to the next digit.

Q9 A value in a number's times table (and beyond).

Q10 $140 = 2 \times 2 \times 5 \times 7 = 2^2 \times 5 \times 7$

Pages 27-28

Quiz 1

Q1 Divide the top and bottom by the same number until they won't divide any more.

Q2 The digit to the right of the last digit in the rounded number. It tells you whether to round up the last digit or not.

Q3 1

Q4 Rewrite them both as improper fractions.

Q5 The second zero

Q6 Rearrange so the front numbers are together and the powers of 10 are together.

Q7 Make the denominators the same.

Q8 53

Q9 The range of values the actual value could have taken before rounding.

Q10 Apply the power to both the top and the bottom of the fraction.

Quiz 2

Q1 A number that all the denominators divide into.

Q2 Identify the position of the last digit in the rounded number.

Q3 True

Q4 1

Q5 $\approx$

Q6 Write the first number over the second and cancel down (if you can).

Q7 0.2

Q8 No — the first number is bigger than 10.

Q9 Half a centimetre

Q10 6 and –6

Answers

Quiz 3

Q1 Subtract the powers

Q2 Chopping off decimal places.

Q3 Write as an addition, turn the integer part into a fraction and add together.

Q4 Rewrite the fractions with a common denominator.

Q5 Round all numbers to 1 or 2 s.f. then do the calculation with the rounded numbers.

Q6 Multiply by 100

Q7 False — the last digit is rounded up.

Q8 1 and 10

Q9 Multiply the tops and bottoms separately.

Q10 Multiply them

Quiz 4

Q1 Divide the top by the bottom.

Q2 9

Q3 Add the powers

Q4 The first digit that isn't zero.

Q5 Turn the second fraction upside down and change the ÷ to ×.

Q6 Add them

Q7 Divide by the bottom of the fraction and multiply by the top.

Q8 13.7

Q9 Overestimate — both numbers in the estimate are bigger than the original numbers.

Q10 143.2

Section 2 — Algebra

Pages 39-40

Quiz 1

Q1 An expression that has an '=' sign in it.

Q2 False — $(2x + 3)^2 = 4x^2 + 12x + 9$

Q3 Multiply out the brackets.

Q4 Add 5 to both sides.

Q5 A collection of numbers, letters and brackets, all multiplied or divided together.

Q6 Work out what the variable is.

Q7 $6x - 15$

Q8 The common factors of the terms in the original expression — i.e. the biggest number and the highest power of each letter that goes into all terms.

Q9 7

Q10 Put bubbles around each term.

Quiz 2

Q1 Multiply each term inside the bracket by the bit outside the bracket.

Q2 $(ab)^2$

Q3 A rule that helps you work something out (has an '=' sign).

Q4 $x^2 + 2x - 3$

Q5 $4x + 3$, where x is Wei's age.

Q6 False —you should do the same thing to both sides.

Q7 Use the function machine in reverse.

Q8 Multiply it out again and check you get the original expression.

Q9 $x = -3$

Q10 $a^2 - b^2 = (a + b)(a - b)$

Quiz 3

Q1 A collection of terms without an '=' sign.

Q2 $-4y + 5$

Q3 Write them out as double brackets.

Q4 16 km

Q5 Add 9 to both sides.

Q6 x^8

Q7 $-2x^2$

Q8 Multiply both sides by 4.

Q9 $(x + 7)(x - 7)$

Q10 4

Quiz 4

Q1 $3p^2q$

Q2 Putting brackets into the expression.

Q3 Get all the x terms on one side of the equals sign, and the numbers on the other side.

Q4 $2x$

Q5 Do the same thing to both sides of the equation. Do the opposite operation to get rid of things you don't want. Keep going until the letter you want is on its own.

Q6 An expression that takes an input value, processes it and produces an output value.

Q7 $\frac{x}{y}$

Q8 13

Q9 First, Outside, Inside, Last

Q10 9

Answers

Pages 47-48

Quiz 1

Q1 Greater than or equal to

Q2 Substitute your x- and y-values into the other equation.

Q3 The same

Q4 Add the previous two terms together.

Q5 False — it means x is less than or equal to 7.

Q6 Multiply so that the coefficients of one of the variables match.

Q7 It flips around.

Q8 The thing you add/subtract each time to get the next term, and the thing you multiply n by in the nth term rule.

Q9 Find an example that doesn't work.

Q10 Yes

Quiz 2

Q1 $x^2 + bx + c = 0$

Q2 Multiply/divide by the same number each time.

Q3 True

Q4 $<$ and $>$

Q5 Multiply the previous term by 3.

Q6 Find values of x that make each bracket equal 0.

Q7 E.g. $2 \times 3 = 6$

Q8 A rule that gives the terms in the sequence when you put in different values of n.

Q9 $(x - 4)(x - 2)$

Q10 Substitute it back into one of the original equations.

Quiz 3

Q1 It means the statement is always true (i.e. it works for all values).

Q2 Add/subtract the same number each time.

Q3 Set the nth term rule equal to the number and solve. The number is in the sequence if n is a whole number.

Q4 x is greater than 2 and less than or equal to 7.

Q5 Match the coefficients of one of the variables, then add/subtract the equations.

Q6 Rearrange one to get the other.

Q7 $x = 2$ and $x = -5$

Q8 Closed circles

Q9 $x^2 + 5x - 6 = 0$

Q10 $2n - 3$

Quiz 4

Q1 In a quadratic sequence, the number you add/subtract changes by the same amount each time, but in a linear sequence it stays the same.

Q2 $x > 6$

Q3 Putting it into two brackets.

Q4 Linear sequence

Q5 $ax + by = c$

Q6 $-4, -3, -2, -1, 0$

Q7 Negative

Q8 Closed circle

Q9 E.g. $3^2 + 4^2 = 9 + 16 = 25 = 5^2$

Q10 3

Section 3 — Graphs

Pages 63-64

Quiz 1

Q1 It goes up from the bottom left with a wiggle in the middle.

Q2 $y = 4$

Q3 Substitute one point into $y = mx + c$ and solve for c.

Q4 The narrow glass.

Q5 The top left quadrant.

Q6 The steepness of the line.

Q7 $y = mx + c$

Q8 The object is moving back towards the starting point.

Q9 The x-values where the graph of the equation crosses the x-axis.

Q10 Go from the given value on one axis straight to the conversion line, then go straight to the other axis and read off the value there.

Quiz 2

Q1 The y-intercept.

Q2 Go along then up (x-coordinate then y-coordinate).

Q3 Plot $y = 5x$ and $y = 3x - 4$ on the graph.

Q4 $y = x$ and $y = -x$

Q5 Negative

Q6 Flat

Q7 No — a straight-line equation can't have an xy term.

Q8 The coefficient of x^2 is negative.

Q9 False — they have different gradients (4 and 3), so they can't be parallel.

Q10 How quickly something is changing.

Answers

Quiz 3

Q1 E.g. use the graph to find 20 km in miles, then multiply by 10.

Q2 $y = 5x$

Q3 A quadratic graph.

Q4 He didn't subtract the coordinates in the same order — he should have worked out 4 – 2 and 3 – 1 or 2 – 4 and 1 – 3.

Q5 $y = \frac{1}{x}$

Q6 Work out the gradient and add the units.

Q7 –2

Q8 The point exactly halfway between the segment's endpoints.

Q9 Speed

Q10 Read off the x-values where the curve crosses the x-axis.

Quiz 4

Q1 Vertical

Q2 Read off the x- and y-values where the graphs intersect.

Q3 Distance from the starting point.

Q4 $y = -2x + 1$

Q5 Substitute x-values into the equation to find y-values.

Q6 Gradient = $\frac{\text{change in } y}{\text{change in } x}$

Q7 A horizontal line at £3 from 0 to 8 people, then a diagonal line with gradient 1 beyond 8 people.

Q8 Put the x-values into the equation to find the y-values. Plot the points. Draw a straight line through them.

Q9 Negative

Q10 That the rate is slower.

Section 4 — Ratio, Proportion and Rates of Change

Pages 73-74

Quiz 1

Q1 a) 1 : 3 b) 7 : 4

Q2 True

Q3 A straight line through the origin, sloping up from left to right.

Q4 Convert 1.5 kg into g.

Q5 11 : 2

Q6 Divide to find the amount for one thing, then multiply to find the amount for the number of things you want.

Q7 False — inverse proportion graphs never go through the origin.

Q8 30 g

Q9 Jar B

Q10 $y = \frac{A}{x}$

Quiz 2

Q1 £15

Q2 Multiply to find the amount for one thing. Divide to find the amount for the number of things you want.

Q3 Multiply all numbers by the same thing to get rid of the decimals, then simplify as normal.

Q4 3 : 8

Q5 It halves.

Q6 Divide £3 by 5 to find the cost of one sticker.

Q7 Write one number on top of the other.

Q8 5 ml

Q9 A = 16

Q10 Multiply the other side of the ratio by the same number.

Quiz 3

Q1 Divide both sides by the number on the left of the ratio.

Q2 $\frac{3}{10}$

Q3 Add up the parts of the ratio.

Q4 E.g. (0, 0) and (2, 5)

Q5 False — they are always in direct proportion.

Q6 Subtract the part you know from the whole.

Q7 A = 5

Q8 A graph that curves down from left to right, and doesn't go through the origin.

Q9 Add to get the total number of parts, then write the part you want over the total.

Q10 £50

Quiz 4

Q1 Multiply all numbers by the same thing to get rid of the fractions.

Q2 It also doubles.

Q3 200 ml

Q4 $y = Ax$

Q5 4 : 3

Q6 1 : 1.5

Q7 Divide to find one part.

Q8 Divide the quantities by 6 to find the amount for one person, then multiply by 10.

Q9 14

Q10 Divide each amount by the price in pence to get the amount per penny. (Or, divide each price by the amount to get the cost per unit.)

Pages 85-86

Quiz 1

Q1 Divide it by 10.

Q2 1 hour 30 minutes

Q3 Multiply and divide by 1000, then choose the sensible answer.

Q4 Divide 18 by 54.

Q5 0.85

Q6 Divide £28 by 80 to find 1% of the original price.

Q7 Multiply and divide by 100 three times, then choose the sensible answer.

Q8 $N = N_0 \times (\text{multiplier})^n$

Q9 300 seconds

Q10 Pressure = $\frac{\text{force}}{\text{area}}$

Answers

Quiz 2

Q1 £4

Q2 Multiply by 60 twice.

Q3 Divide the first number by the second number, then multiply by 100.

Q4 The initial amount

Q5 Compound decay

Q6 N/m^2 (or pascals)

Q7 Twice

Q8 Time = $\frac{\text{distance}}{\text{speed}}$

Q9 4300 ml

Q10 % change = $\frac{\text{change}}{\text{original}} \times 100$

Quiz 3

Q1 1000

Q2 Speed = $\frac{\text{distance}}{\text{time}}$

Q3 Convert the percentage into a decimal.

Q4 Triangle: M over D × V

Q5 1.25

Q6 11 pounds

Q7 Find the loss — subtract the new amount from the original amount.

Q8 Find 2% of the original value in the account, then multiply by 3.

Q9 205 minutes

Q10 Write the amount as a percentage of the original value.

Quiz 4

Q1 12

Q2 100

Q3 Find the percentage of the original amount and add to or subtract from the original value. Or, work out the multiplier and multiply the original value by it.

Q4 1.05

Q5 1000

Q6 200 N/m^2

Q7 6 km

Q8 When a percentage of the original value is paid at regular intervals.

Q9 Multiply and divide by 10 twice, then choose the sensible answer.

Q10 20%

Section 5 — Shapes and Area

Pages 95-96

Quiz 1

Q1 False — a rectangle has 4 equal angles of 90°.

Q2 That all three sides are the same.

Q3 The top number

Q4 True

Q5 A shape with all sides and angles the same.

Q6 Scale factor = $\frac{\text{new length}}{\text{old length}}$

Q7 Order 1

Q8 1 pair

Q9 (1, –5)

Q10 3 lines

Quiz 2

Q1 Shapes that are the same size and shape.

Q2 Order 4

Q3 The shape gets smaller.

Q4 1 line

Q5 Yes — they are the same shape in different sizes.

Q6 2 pairs

Q7 Where the two parts of a shape on either side of a mirror line fold exactly together.

Q8 A corresponding side needs to match up.

Q9 60°

Q10 The angle, direction and centre of rotation.

Quiz 3

Q1 The scale factor and centre of enlargement.

Q2 8 sides

Q3 True

Q4 The direction

Q5 Parallelogram

Q6 2 lines

Q7 Scalene

Q8 SSS, ASA, SAS and RHS

Q9 Order 2

Q10 3 units to the right and 2 units down.

Quiz 4

Q1 2 pairs

Q2 3

Q3 9 lines

Q4 The equation of the mirror line.

Q5 Equilateral triangle

Q6 Order 1

Q7 False — the angle must be between the two sides for the triangles to be congruent.

Q8 18 units

Q9 Proportional

Q10 1 line

Pages 105-106

Quiz 1

Q1 True

Q2 The space inside a 3D shape.

Q3 Plan

Q4 Volume of a pyramid $= \frac{1}{3} \times \text{base area} \times h_v$

Q5 4 vertices, 6 edges and 4 faces.

Q6 Length of an arc $= \frac{x}{360} \times \text{circumference of circle}$

Q7 3 cm^2

Q8 Subtract the volume of the removed cone from the volume of the original cone.

Q9 The distance around the outside.

Q10 Surface area of cone = $\pi rl + \pi r^2$

Quiz 2

Q1 Find the area of its net.

Q2 Area of parallelogram = base × vertical height

Q3 Minor segment

Q4 The circumference of a circle.

Q5 Cone

Answers

Q6 Work out each volume separately and make sure they are in the same units.

Q7 The surface area of a sphere.

Q8 Triangular prism

Q9 Volume of a cylinder = $\pi r^2 h$

Q10 Volume

Quiz 3

Q1 Volume of a sphere = $\frac{4}{3}\pi r^3$

Q2 The total area of all faces of a 3D shape.

Q3 Major sector

Q4 Area of a trapezium $= \frac{1}{2}(a + b) \times$ vertical height

Q5 24 cm^3

Q6 1 more

Q7 Volume of a prism = $A \times L$

Q8 The area of the net is equal to the surface area of the 3D shape.

Q9 A frustum is what's left when the top of a cone is cut off parallel to its base.

Q10 The area of a circle.

Quiz 4

Q1 How fast volume is changing.

Q2 The surface area of a cylinder.

Q3 Split it into triangles and quadrilaterals, work out their areas and then add them together.

Q4 8 cm^3

Q5 8 vertices, 12 edges and 6 faces

Q6 Volume of a cone = $\frac{1}{3}\pi r^2 h_v$

Q7 Front elevation, side elevation and plan.

Q8 Area of a sector $= \frac{x}{360} \times$ area of full circle

Q9 The shape folded out flat.

Q10 Sphere

Section 6 — Angles and Geometry

Pages 115-116

Quiz 1

Q1 Angles that are less than 90°.

Q2 Roughly sketch and label the triangle.

Q3 A circle

Q4 Lines that meet at a right angle.

Q5 False — angles on a straight line add up to 180°.

Q6 Draw two arcs from the initial point that cross the initial line. Place the point of the compass on each intersection and draw two intersecting arcs. Join this intersection to the initial point with a straight line.

Q7 Sum of interior angles $= (n - 2) \times 180°$ (n is the number of sides)

Q8 Protractor

Q9 104°

Q10 Increase the compass settings.

Quiz 2

Q1 2

Q2 With the compass point on the end of the initial line, draw one arc crossing the line and a second arc roughly 60° around from the initial line. Keeping the compass settings the same, put the point on the intersection of the first arc and the initial line, and draw another arc that intersects the second arc. Join this intersection to the end of the initial line with a straight line.

Q3 A line or region that shows all points that fit a given rule.

Q4 Obtuse

Q5 Exterior angle = $\frac{360°}{n}$ (n is the number of sides)

Q6 The base line

Q7 210°

Q8 The locus of points a fixed distance from a given line.

Q9 False — vertically opposite angles are equal.

Q10 Bisects it.

Quiz 3

Q1 A sausage shape — it has two straight sides with the ends joined by semicircles.

Q2 180°

Q3 Measure the angles with a protractor and mark with dots.

Q4 True

Q5 Angles that are more than 180°.

Q6 Join the points, and label the sides and angles.

Q7 Alternate angles

Q8 Position the protractor with the base line along one of the angle lines.

Q9 360°

Q10 The locus of points equidistant from Points A and B.

Quiz 4

Q1 Lines that are always the same distance apart and never meet.

Q2 True

Q3 90°

Q4 2

Q5 Set the compasses to each side length and draw an arc from each end of the base line.

Q6 130°

Q7 360°

Q8 The locus of points a fixed distance from a given point.

Answers

Q9 Subtract the exterior angle from 180°.

Q10 With the point of the compass on the point where the lines meet, draw an arc on each line. Then draw another arc from each of the first arcs. Join this intersection to the point where the lines meet with a straight line.

Pages 125-126

Quiz 1

Q1 085°

Q2 The hypotenuse

Q3 True

Q4 Top: horizontal distance moved. Bottom: vertical distance moved.

Q5 Square both numbers.

Q6 $\frac{1}{2}$

Q7 Label the sides O, A and H.

Q8 12.5 km

Q9 $\tan x = \frac{\text{opp}}{\text{adj}}$

Q10 $\begin{pmatrix} -2 \\ 14 \end{pmatrix}$

Quiz 2

Q1 $\sin x = \frac{\text{opp}}{\text{hyp}}$, $\cos x = \frac{\text{adj}}{\text{hyp}}$, $\tan x = \frac{\text{opp}}{\text{adj}}$

Q2 From point B.

Q3 Parallel

Q4 Multiply by the map scale.

Q5 $a^2 + b^2 = c^2$

Q6 It changes size.

Q7 $\frac{1}{\sqrt{2}}$

Q8 $\cos x = \frac{\text{adj}}{\text{hyp}}$

Q9 $\begin{pmatrix} 2 \\ 8 \end{pmatrix}$

Q10 5 cm by 8 cm

Quiz 3

Q1 

Q2 Divide by the map scale.

Q3 False — Pythagoras' theorem only works on right-angled triangles.

Q4 Clockwise

Q5 $\begin{pmatrix} -1 \\ 8 \end{pmatrix}$

Q6 $\sin x = \frac{\text{opp}}{\text{hyp}}$

Q7 1 cm : 20 km

Q8 It changes size and reverses direction.

Q9 See which two sides are involved, then choose the formula that uses them.

Q10 tan 60°

Quiz 4

Q1 Adjacent

Q2 Size and direction

Q3 Take the square root.

Q4 4 m by 3 m

Q5 Take the inverse.

Q6 500 m

Q7 O / T × A (triangle)

Q8 $\begin{pmatrix} -18 \\ -6 \end{pmatrix}$

Q9 1

Q10 $\underline{a} - \underline{b}$

Section 7 — Probability and Statistics

Pages 135-136

Quiz 1

Q1 Impossible

Q2 Relative frequency $= \frac{\text{Frequency}}{\text{Number of times you tried the experiment}}$

Q3 Multiply along the branches.

Q4 True

Q5 0.2

Q6 The universal set.

Q7 How many times you'd expect something to happen in a certain number of trials.

Q8 P(A and B) = P(A) × P(B)

Q9 Biased

Q10 The overlap of the circles.

Quiz 2

Q1 Subtract P(event happens) from 1.

Q2 Every outcome is equally likely.

Q3 The universal set.

Q4 True

Q5 To record results when experiments have more than one step.

Q6 One event happening doesn't affect the probability of the other event happening.

Q7 Inside circle A, but not in the overlap.

Q8 A diagram that shows all possible outcomes.

Q9 0.4

Q10 A collection of elements (written in curly brackets).

Answers

Quiz 3

Q1 $\frac{1}{6}$

Q2 The total number of things.

Q3 A table with rows labelled 1, 2 and 3 and columns labelled 1, 2 and 3. The sum of the row and column labels goes in each cell.

Q4 4

Q5 Do the experiment more times.

Q6 Certain

Q7 Elements that are in both set A and set B.

Q8 1

Q9 15 times

Q10 0.45

Quiz 4

Q1 0.2

Q2 1

Q3 15

Q4 Probability $= \frac{\text{Number of ways for something to happen}}{\text{Total number of possible outcomes}}$

Q5 Some outcomes are more likely than others.

Q6 P(A or B) = P(A) + P(B)

Q7 0.55

Q8 Expected frequency = probability × number of trials

Q9 0.08

Q10 Inside the rectangle but outside the circles.

Pages 149-150

Quiz 1

Q1 Give each member of the population a number. Make a list of random numbers. Pick the members of the population with those numbers.

Q2 Add up the numbers to find the total.

Q3 The value of each symbol.

Q4 Data described in words.

Q5 Arrange the data in size order. The median is the middle value.

Q6 A line that goes through or near most points on a scatter graph.

Q7 30

Q8 Dual bar charts and composite bar charts.

Q9 Points form an upward slope and they make a fairly straight line.

Q10 Multiply the number of each category by the frequency, then add up these values. Then use the formula: mean $= \frac{\text{total (category} \times \text{frequency)}}{\text{total frequency}}$

Quiz 2

Q1 Frequency

Q2 Data that can only take exact values.

Q3 Points form a downward slope but they don't line up neatly.

Q4 E.g. Some groups could have been excluded. / It might not be big enough.

Q5 Subtract the lowest value from the highest value.

Q6 Sales would be on the vertical axis and time (in weeks) would be on the horizontal axis.

Q7 8°

Q8 Multiply each mid-interval value by the frequency for that category.

Q9 The whole group you want to find out about.

Q10 Interpolation

Quiz 3

Q1 The most common value.

Q2 How closely two things are related.

Q3 360°

Q4 Comparing data sets.

Q5 Give each pupil a number.

Q6 The highest and lowest class boundaries.

Q7 Interpolation

Q8 Add/subtract using the given information.

Q9 They are clear and easy to understand / easy to answer / fair.

Q10 Data described using numbers.

Quiz 4

Q1 Composite bar chart

Q2 Ignore them.

Q3 Add up the values and divide by the number of values.

Q4 True

Q5 A basic repeating pattern over time.

Q6 Work out which value is the middle one. The category containing that value is the median.

Q7 Divide 360° by the total number of things.

Q8 Extrapolation

Q9 The values in set A are more consistent than those in set B.

Q10 How many things there are in each category.